Furniture at Temple Newsam House and Lotherton Hall

297

Furniture at Temple Newsam House and Lotherton Hall

Christopher Gilbert

A catalogue of the Leeds collection
In two volumes

Volume I

Published jointly by the National Art-Collections Fund
and the Leeds Art Collections Fund
1978

Published jointly by the National Art-Collections
Fund and the Leeds Art Collections Fund

Made and printed in Great Britain by
Lund Humphries, Bradford and London
Designed by Godfrey Meekin

ISBN 0 9503334 1 7

To my Mother and Father

ACKNOWLEDGEMENTS

During the preparation of this catalogue, which has spanned ten years, I have accumulated numerous debts of gratitude to archivists, librarians, colleagues in the museum profession, antique dealers, auctioneers, the previous owners of items in the collection and experts in various fields. Many individuals are acknowledged in the appropriate entry, but I wish in particular to thank Christopher Hutchinson who, with patience and great skill, produced nearly all the photographs.

I received invaluable guidance from David Barker whilst researching the clocks; Nicholas Goodison advised on the ormolu wares; Boyen Y. F. Li kindly checked the entries on Oriental furniture and John Malden solved most of the heraldic problems while Miss Karin Walton and Michael Sheppard assisted over identifying upholstery materials. Miss Pamela Hall and Mrs Pauline Agius helped to research and classify the Pratt collection of furniture trade catalogues and Miss Susan Bourne performed a similar service in respect of the furniture which Gillows supplied to Parlington Hall. My colleagues at Leeds have proved a constant source of inspiration and information, merely listing their names is a poor return for their input, but must regrettably suffice: Anthony Wells-Cole; Dr Terry Friedman; Robert Rowe; Miss Jean English; Jacob Simon, James Lomax and Richard Fawcett.

Others who helped me both in person and by correspondence include Francis Bamford; Geoffrey Beard; Peter Brears; Timothy Clifford; Anthony Coleridge; John Cornforth; Benno Forman; Dr Ivan Hall; John Hardy; Edward Joy; Mrs Pat Kirkham; Dr Derek Linstrum; Simon Redburn; Cyril Staal; Colin Streeter and David Thornton. Welcome comments about the continental furniture were received from Geoffrey de Bellaigue; Miss Frances Buckland; Hugh Honour; Professor T. H. Lunsingh Scheurleer; Peter Thornton; M. Pierre Verlet and Sir Francis Watson.

Space, not ingratitude, precludes the naming of every person who has made a contribution of value, but the following cannot be omitted: Bill Audsley; Victor Chinnery; Dr Penelope Eames; Francis Egerton; David Feather; Lady Gascoigne; Tony Harrison; John and Helena Hayward; Francis Johnson; Brian Kern; Ronald Lee; George Levy; Frank Lumb; John Partridge; Jerome Phillips; Christopher Pratt; Henry Rubin; Lady Sandys; Ivan Sparkes; Ron Turner and Clive Wainwright. I am very conscious of countless letters and memoranda in the Temple Newsam furniture archive recording information solicited from well-wishers all over the world: this catalogue is underpinned by their knowledge and I wish to express my warmest thanks for their helpful interest.

Miss Barbara Thompson cheerfully typed, and following revisions, often retyped my lengthy manuscript; Dr Dorothy Rayner volunteered to double-check the proofs and Brian Cawthray has carried the burden of seeing a complicated work of this nature through the press. I would like also to express my profound appreciation to George Black and Martin Arnold, chairman and treasurer respectively of the L.A.C.F., for their confidence in the project and to Brinsley Ford and Mrs Sheila Folkard, chairman and secretary of the N.A.C.F., for their excellent support. The fifty guarantors, whose imaginative patronage has made this publication possible, are named in a separate 'roll of honour'; besides earning my personal gratitude they will be remembered by everyone devoted to the study of fine furniture.

C.G.G.

PREFACE

The idea that the National Art-Collections Fund and the Leeds Art Collections Fund jointly should sponsor the Catalogue of Furniture at Temple Newsam House and Lotherton Hall had much to commend it. The Leeds collection is one of the finest in public ownership and the N.A.C.F. has played an important part in the acquisition of many of the most outstanding pieces in it. Happily Christopher Gilbert, Principal Keeper of Temple Newsam, had completed his research and all was ready for publication in 1978. It seemed appropriate therefore that the N.A.C.F., to mark its 75th anniversary, should go into partnership with its younger cousin, the L.A.C.F., to ensure the production of a catalogue worthy of its contents. There is considerable family likeness between the two charities, not only in their names, but more significantly in their work. The L.A.C.F. has also contributed much to the Leeds furniture collection the growth of which, indeed, it has been able to watch very closely from its Yorkshire headquarters. Less than ten years younger – it sees its 66th birthday in 1978 – it is older than the collection itself, for this has been lovingly and skilfully put together in little over half a century and mainly since the last war.

Finally, we would like to thank the guarantors who, in a spirit of art patronage, are supporting this imaginative venture, and also the Midland Bank Ltd who, as a special gesture of goodwill, have very generously waived their considerable charges for arranging the banking facilities.

Brinsley Ford, Chairman of the N.A.C.F.
George Black, Chairman of the L.A.C.F.

Guarantors

The following have underwritten the capital required to finance this book:

The Rt. Hon. the Earl of Halifax
President Leeds Art Collections Fund

Brinsley Ford, Esq
Chairman National Art-Collections Fund

W. L. Banks, Esq
H. Blairman & Sons Ltd
R. L. Bridle, Esq
The British Antique Dealers' Association Ltd
Paul Broomhall, Esq
Mrs. G. Brotherton-Ratcliffe
Michael Bucks, Esq

Arnold J. Burton, Esq
Raymond M. Burton, Esq
Stanley H. Burton, Esq
Christie, Manson & Woods Ltd
The Rt. Hon. Lord Faringdon
David Feather, Esq
J. P. Ferguson, Esq
James S. Fox, Esq
Mr and Mrs Burton Friedman
Godden of Worthing Ltd
Lionel Golodetz, Esq
Nicholas P. Goodison, Esq
The Rt. Hon. the Viscount Gough
L. V. Hart, Esq
Philip Hewat-Jaboor, Esq
Sir Antony Hornby
Hotspur Ltd
Leeds Art Collections Fund
Miss Janet E. Leng
Miss Mildred Lockyer
Charles Lumb & Sons Ltd
Percy Lund, Humphries & Co Ltd
David McAlpine, Esq
Richard Milhender, Esq
Miss Matilda Mitchell
National Art-Collections Fund
Partridge (Fine Arts) Ltd
Mrs Evelyn Pedley
Phillips of Hitchin (Antiques) Ltd
Cyril S. Reddihough, Esq
Mrs Ingrid Roscoe
David B. Ryott, Esq
Simon Sainsbury, Esq
H. M. Sassoon Charitable Trust
Alan E. Shave, Esq
Philip Shelbourne, Esq
Smiths "The Rink" Ltd
Paul Stobart, Esq
Major A. H. Turnbull
N. J. L. Webster, Esq
Dr R. B. Welch

Addendum

E. J. Arnold & Son Ltd, Christie, Manson & Woods Ltd and Phillips International Fine Art Auctioneers, Leeds each donated the sum of £250 to cover the unforeseen cost of publishing the Titus Salt furniture from Milner Field.

EXPLANATIONS

ARRANGEMENT

The furniture is numbered in sequence throughout the two volumes. As the contents page indicates the collection is catalogued under four main heads: English, Continental, Colonial and Oriental and Documentary Material. Within the English category (which includes Irish and Scottish pieces) the furniture is sub-divided alphabetically according to types and chronologically through each section, following the familiar pattern established by Ralph Edwards's *Dictionary of English Furniture*, 1954. However, it should be pointed out that the chairs are preceded by entries describing suites of seat furniture while five coherent sub-groups together with unregistered furniture from the chapel at Lotherton and the Aberford Almshouses are catalogued separately at the end of the English section. With the exception of the Salt furniture by Marsh and Jones (acquired only at proof stage), these detached groups are fully cross-referenced in the main body of the catalogue. Also, French musical instruments and electric light fittings will be found under the relevant English heading with appropriate cross references under their country of origin. The Continental furniture and the Colonial and Oriental pieces are arranged chronologically, not by type, within each national division. The final part embraces manuscript designs, casts and furniture trade catalogues.

MEASUREMENTS

These are given in both centimetres and inches, the English equivalents, which follow the metric, are enclosed in brackets. Measurements are the maximum in the direction indicated H. (height); W. (width); D. (depth); Diam. (diameter); L. (length) except for the width and depth of chairs, stools, settees and daybeds which are measured at seat rail level.

INSCRIPTIONS

Stamps, brand marks, maker's initials and impressed names on the furniture have been liberally transcribed. Because the dimensions vary greatly, some of the facsimiles (drawn specially by Andrew Spencer) are not reproduced actual size, in these cases a scale is stated.

LITERATURE REFERENCES (LIT)

References to and illustrations of furniture in successive guide books to Temple Newsam and Lotherton Hall are not recorded. Very slight allusions are also omitted.

EXHIBITIONS (EXH)

The annual 'Acquisitions of the Year' exhibitions held at Leeds since 1934 are not cited.

PROVENANCE (PROV)

Exceptional pains have been taken to elucidate the origins of and follow the movement of items through the trade. Dealers are consistently recorded under one name although certain firms have slightly altered their style over the years. To avoid ambiguity between private individuals and members of the trade the word 'Antiques' is sometimes appended in brackets.

MUSEUM NUMBER

Each catalogue entry ends with the museum accession number in square brackets.

BIBLIOGRAPHY

There is no bibliography since full details of all relevant publications, including sale catalogues and exhibition catalogues are given in the text.

ABBREVIATIONS

The following abbreviations have been used:

B.A.D.A.	British Antique Dealers' Association
D.E.F.	R. Edwards, *The Dictionary of English Furniture*, 3 vols, 1954
L.A.C.	*Leeds Arts Calendar*
L.A.C.F.	Leeds Art Collections Fund
L.G. & R.F.	C. Gilbert, *Late Georgian and Regency Furniture*, 1972
N.A.C.F.	National Art-Collections Fund
T.N.	Temple Newsam House (occasional)
V. & A.	Victoria and Albert Museum, London
Y.A.S.	Yorkshire Archaeological Society
Y.R.S.	Yorkshire Record Series

CONTENTS
of Volumes I and II

INTRODUCTION

The formation of the collection

Leeds City Council possesses one of the few furniture collections in public ownership which is both large and important enough to justify a full catalogue. This has not come about through a single spectacular benefaction as chanced when Durham County Council acquired the Bowes Museum in 1956 or Merseyside County Council assumed responsibility for the Lady Lever Art Gallery in 1978; the Leeds collection has evolved over a period of more than sixty years, so besides illuminating the history of taste and art patronage its stratification reflects fashions in collecting.

The Art Gallery

The City Art Gallery had been in existence for twenty-five years before the newly-founded Leeds Art Collections Fund initiated a policy of buying furniture as a supporting cast for the paintings. At this date only rather grandiloquent continental furniture was considered appropriate for a municipal art gallery; accordingly, between 1913 and 1927, the L.A.C.F. presented no fewer than six suitably palatial carved and gilt Italian tables with marble tops, an English side table of similar character and a French copy of the ostentatious *commode medallier* made by Antoine Gaudreaux for Versailles in 1738. Thus, the earliest phase of collecting just interlocks with the Victorian passion, expressed so vividly at Mentmore Towers and Arundel Castle, for flamboyant continental decorative art and exact reproductions of well known French masterpieces.

In 1925 Sam Wilson, a wealthy mill owner, bequeathed to the city, along with a notable collection of modern oil paintings and sculpture, some twenty pieces of furniture from his villa, Rutland Lodge in the Potternewton suburb of Leeds. This legacy reflects the taste of a typical Edwardian connoisseur buying at a time when antique furniture was just beginning to interest conventional collectors. Its art-historical value is much enhanced by the survival of Sam Wilson's private notebooks. In 1907 he ordered seven expensive examples of reproduction French cabinet furniture from Gillow & Co., but his most extravagant purchase was a boudoir grand piano shown by Erard at the Paris Exhibition of 1900. The lavish marquetry case and ormolu mounts by Jansen are derived from Riesener's celebrated *Bureau du Roi*, so this remarkable instrument creates an important cultural link with the heroic age of International Exhibitions of Arts and Manufactures. Sam Wilson also furnished Rutland Lodge with modest antiques reflecting the currently popular Chippendale, Adam and Sheraton styles, carefully noting the trade source and price of each item in his inventory. Very few of these domestic pieces are in anything approaching original condition; they form in fact an instructive anthology of the beautified and made-up furniture stocked by most Edwardian dealers and art furnishers: the distinction between genuine and reproduction antiques was little regarded by the average collector of Sam Wilson's generation.

An exhibition titled *English Furniture 1600–1800* featuring treasures from Yorkshire country houses and reputable local collections was held at the City Art Gallery in 1930. Although several of the loans were acquired long afterwards by gift or bequest this event, far from inspiring a new attitude towards diversifying the permanent collection, proved to be a requiem for the always desultory and now obsolete policy of stocking the Art Gallery with furniture.

Temple Newsam House

When the Hon. E. F. Lindley Wood who, as Lord Halifax, was to inherit from his father two more Yorkshire country houses, Hickleton and Garrowby, decided to give up Temple Newsam in 1922 he offered the house and park to Leeds Corporation for a nominal £30,000. At that time Temple Newsam lay outside the city boundary, but due largely to the zeal of Alderman Sir Charles Wilson, the council was persuaded to grasp this unique opportunity of acquiring an estate of 900 acres which included a famous Tudor-Jacobean mansion where Lord Darnley was born.

Before Temple Newsam passed into public ownership a seven days auction sale was ordered, and for the next fifteen years the house remained more or less an empty shell through which visitors were conducted in herds. Fortunately, Edward Wood took many excellent paintings and some of the finest early-Georgian furniture to Hickleton Hall, near Doncaster and he left a residue of the art collection behind as a gift to the citizens of Leeds. Furthermore, various lots were purchased by the Council so, while the house contained little of serious interest, it was not completely denuded. The assorted furniture presented by the late Lord Halifax included a splendid pair of rococo girandoles 'with hunting ornaments' commissioned for the Long Gallery about 1750; a large suite of early-Regency hall chairs; a pair of mid-eighteenth century 28 inch library globes; a picturesque Dutch sleigh; an upright grand piano by John Broadwood & Son, styled to harmonize with the decor of the Chinese drawing room; several clocks and the furnishings from the private chapel created by G. F. Bodley in 1877. To this repertoire can be added some antiques acquired cheaply by Leeds Corporation at the auction sale to provide a skeleton display when, a year later, the house opened to the public. Leaving aside ordinary household articles purchased to furnish a caretaker's flat, Leeds secured a seventeenth century Flemish cupboard; a Victorian oak bedstead; two late-Regency sideboard tables; a running sideboard; two

Edwardian 'Chippendale' library tables and various fire-irons.[1] Until Temple Newsam was launched as a country house museum this scanty static collection, supported by a show of paintings, tapestries, china and domestic paraphernalia was all that greeted visitors.

Bills from fashionable tradesmen such as Thomas Chippendale, William Hallett, John Cobb and John Linnell preserved amongst the Temple Newsam archive reveal that the descendants of Sir Arthur Ingram (created Viscounts Irwin in 1661) were discerning patrons.[2] Most of the furniture they commissioned has vanished, its only memorial now being entries in old inventories, the unillustrated 1922 sale catalogue or a shadowy presence in photographs of heavily furnished interiors at Temple Newsam published by Fletcher Moss in 1910.[3] While it must be acknowledged that unique opportunities were missed at the auction, enough indigenous furniture survives to form an interesting strand of continuity and, in retrospect, unless bidding had been very discerning, Temple Newsam could well have become encumbered with an accumulation of mediocre furniture which inhibited its future development as a museum of decorative art. In the event ample space existed to build up a significant collection. No attempt has been made to retrieve objects with a Temple Newsam ancestry, apart from a long term and largely successful bid to trace and acquire the magnificent parade furniture supplied by James Pascall for the Gallery in 1746.[4]

Philip Hendy, who became Director of the Leeds Art Gallery in 1934, first appreciated the potential of Temple Newsam as a country house museum. Although externally the building presents a stern Tudor-Jacobean countenance the interior, which has been modernized by successive generations of owners, expresses a richly varied architectural character, yielding an appropriate setting for furnishings of almost every period from 1520 to 1912 when the South East Room was remodelled by Lenygon and Morant as a library in the early-Georgian taste. By staging an imaginative loan exhibition of English pictures and furniture, opened by Lord Harlech in 1938, Philip Hendy was able to demonstrate that Temple Newsam functioned admirably as a museum of decorative art. Following this popular success, Frank Fulford, a wealthy local connoisseur, offered to pay for equipping the glamorous Chinese drawing room with Sheraton furniture supported by a dazzling array of oriental jades and gold boxes from his own collection, a benefaction which so impressed the City Council that they decided to refurbish the principal rooms and vote a modest purchase fund.

One of the most difficult problems was furnishing the Gallery, for the grandeur of the room demanded furniture of equal magnificence and it required a suite rather than a collection of unmatched chairs. The exceptionally large gilt and floral needlework suite consisting of twenty chairs, four sofas and a day-bed commissioned in 1746 by Henry, 7th Viscount Irwin for his new salon had been withheld from the Temple Newsam sale and lent by Lord Halifax to his brother-in-law, Lord Bingley, at Bramham Park some ten miles away. The entire suite was borrowed for the reopening exhibition and shortly afterwards Lord Halifax announced that he intended to sell it. Although the opportunity to acquire seat furniture of comparable splendour might never recur, there appeared to be little prospect of securing it for Temple Newsam and thus save it from being split up. However, a grant of £1,500, the largest ever made by the National Art-Collections Fund for furniture, and an appeal to four local benefactors raised £5,000 which the owner generously agreed to accept. This achievement established a crucial standard of excellence for future acquisitions.

It is worth reviewing the steps taken to furnish the Gallery for, although unique in itself, the exercise offers an insight into how the wider collection has been built up. As previously explained the resplendent girandoles never left their original setting and just before the war the needlework suite returned to, as Philip Hendy lyrically wrote, 'form an everlasting herbacious border around the great room'. During hostilities the mansion committee felt they 'must more than ever keep before the public visual evidence of the civilization to defend which the war was being fought' and with timely help from Sir George and Lady Martin the furnishing programme continued. They paid for a flamboyant rococo side table formerly at Bramshill and a superb looking glass in the manner of Matthias Lock from the Duke of Kent's collection, both of which are perfectly attuned to the adjacent girandoles. Lady Martin also presented a fluent but so far unprovenanced pair of mid-eighteenth century marble topped side tables now placed against the side walls. In 1943 a dignified pair of Palladian hall settees, later proved to have been made in 1731 by James Moore the Younger to the design of William Kent for Sherborne House, Gloucestershire, were acquired to occupy the spacious Jacobean window bays opposite the imposing twin chimneypieces also based on one of William Kent's engravings.

At this time the price of antique furniture was falling, a downward trend which continued during the post-war glut of country house sales. The foundation of the collection was laid in these halcyon years when, although funds were limited and not always available at the right moment, masterpieces were flooding the art market. The Hickleton Hall sale held in 1947 included a lively pair of early rococo console tables with ornamental gesso tops and eight opulent gilt candlestands commissioned for the Gallery at Temple Newsam; the tables were presented shortly afterwards by Colonel F. E. Tetley and reinstated in their original positions against the north piers, but the candlestands, which fetched only £29 each, escaped, and it was not until 1976 that four were traced and retrieved at a cost of £16,000; the companions are known to be in a private German collection. When, in 1958, a handsome pair of eagle console tables, probably designed by Henry Flitcroft for Wentworth Woodhouse, Yorkshire

---

[1] *Temple Newsam Heirlooms*, Leeds Art Galleries Exhibition Catalogue, 1972.

[2] C. G. Gilbert, 'The Temple Newsam Furniture Bills', *Furniture History*, III (1967) pp.16–28. C. G. Gilbert, 'Newly-discovered Furniture by William Hallett', *Connoisseur*, Dec. 1964, pp.224–5.

[3] *Pilgrimages to Old Homes*, V (1910).

[4] C. G. Gilbert, 'The Temple Newsam Suite of Early-Georgian Gilt Furniture', *Connoisseur*, Feb. 1968, pp.84–8.

were added, the furnishing of this incomparable room was almost complete. A severe disappointment has been the failure to trace a ravishing pair of rococo side tables with dragon-head supports and pierced aprons centering on satyr masks auctioned in 1922. However, watchful patience may eventually be rewarded and in 1974 a chance was gratefully accepted to buy instead a majestic pair of documented console tables and oval pier glasses ordered by the Earl of Coventry from Vile and Cobb for Croome Court in 1760.

This sequence of acquisitions spanning forty years, suggests some underlying principles which have contributed to the formation of the collection. Attention has always been paid to illustrious quality and the placing of each object within a room scheme so as to create a coherent ensemble – the process has aptly been likened to playing 'happy families'. Throughout the thirty public rooms an attempt has been made to contrive an overall pattern which conveys a vivid impression of the evolution of fashionable taste. For example, the chinoiserie pieces, although widely scattered, interact to illustrate the various phases of European interest in the orient, extending from a primitive early seventeenth century japanned cabinet, through the William and Mary vogue for florid many-drawered japanned cabinets raised on gilt stands, to Giles Grendey's colourful Spanish export furniture and so on to sophisticated Chinese Chippendale lattice back chairs and the Regency Court style represented by the frivolous decor of Lady Hertford's sunny Chinese drawing room. This theme is visually and intellectually reinforced by items of genuine oriental porcelain and the European wares they inspired as well as chinoiserie silver and textiles.

The temptation to buy a multiplicity of respectable but undistinguished furniture to stock the empty rooms at Temple Newsam was avoided because, at the outbreak of war, the mansion became a refuge for all the pictures from the Art Gallery and many country house owners whose homes were requisitioned lent their furniture for display at Temple Newsam rather than commit it to store. The return of these substantial loans from Castle Howard, Beningbrough Hall, Farnley Hall, Newburgh Priory, Methley Hall, Sir William Burrell, Lady Muriel Barclay-Harvey and the Society for the Protection of Ancient Buildings, has been geared to the growth of the permanent collection. Several were not recalled until the 1950s or 1960s while others are still being repatriated as additional space is needed. This flexible arrangement has helped to sustain a discriminating acquisitions policy.

From the earliest days Temple Newsam has received many gifts and bequests. In 1947 Viscount Allendale handed over a complete early-Tudor panelled room from Bretton Park, near Wakefield, incorporating an historic bed and a fixed cupboard carved with armorials and pictorial panels in the Gothic taste; the woodwork, documented in an inventory of 1542, was re-erected in a room on the west wing which preserves architectural features dating from Henry VIII's reign. Thus, while salvaging period interiors runs contrary to the principles which have inspired the growth of the collection this was a perfectly legitimate project. Another memorable gift which confirmed the post-war status of Temple Newsam was Sir Henry Price's presentation in 1950 of the famous Duke of Leeds daybed and sofa, generally regarded as the most sumptuous late-Stuart upholstered seat furniture in existence. Two more notably generous gifts were an impressive pedestal organ clock by George Pyke from Mrs. Ina Kitson Clark (1954) and a Regency state bed commissioned for Clifton Castle, Yorkshire contributed by Mrs. J. H. Curzon-Herrick in 1963.

Over the years local collectors have bequeathed substantial legacies of Georgian furniture to Leeds, the most important being received from Mrs. Frank Gott (1941); Agnes and Norman Lupton (1953), David Dunstan Schofield (1962), Frank Savery (1966)[5] and Sir George Martin (1976). These bequests, while containing excellent individual pieces, consist mainly of medium quality domestic furniture forming an important stratum which otherwise would be under-represented, for the purchase fund has seldom been used to acquire furniture of provincial character. Recent experience suggests that, following changes in the tax laws, major pieces accepted by the government in satisfaction of estate duty or in lieu of capital transfer tax may in future greatly enhance the primary collection. During the last two years Leeds has been allocated an elegant walnut bureau from Herriard Park bearing the previously unrecorded trade label of John Gatehouse, London and a luxurious serpentine commode enriched with ormolu mounts and brass grilles attributed to John Cobb's workshop.

Although gifts and bequests have played a valuable role it is furniture acquired by purchase (frequently with the aid of government grants or assistance from art charities and private benefactors) which forms the backbone of the collection. During the post war decade country house sales provided a happy hunting ground; for instance, between 1947 and 1950 important pieces were bought at the Hickleton Hall, Lowther Castle, Howsham Hall, Swinton Park, Boynton Hall and Rothiemay Castle sales. At the same time, and throughout the 1950s, other key items such as the massive Gothick library table made for Pomfret Castle, the Channon commode from Southwick Park, a pair of Palladian side tables designed by Matthias Lock for Ditchley House and the Wentworth Woodhouse console tables, together with a richly carved pair of sconces and a side table, both in the manner of Benjamin Goodison – all of which could go straight into any museum in the world – were obtained from London and Harrogate dealers.

Following the decline of country house sales Leeds has come to rely increasingly on the co-operation of leading antique dealers, several of whom regularly offer Temple Newsam first refusal of outstanding objects at specially low prices. Advantage has also been taken of the estate duty legislation to secure desirable pieces on very helpful terms. Acquisitions over the last twenty years, which compare favourably with those of the first twenty years, include a rococo bed with contemporary damask hangings from Aldby Hall (1959), the celebrated library table supplied by Thomas Chippendale to Harewood House (1965), a

---

[5] Bequeathed in memory of his grandfather, George Brooke of Huddersfield.

labelled suite of scarlet japanned furniture made by Giles Grendey for the Spanish trade (1970), a majestic pair of console tables and pier glasses commissioned in 1760 from Vile and Cobb for Croome Court (1974), a fully documented Gobelins tapestry sofa and four armchairs from Moor Park (1975) and the four rococo candlestands ordered for the Long Gallery (1976). None of these masterpieces has been deliberately uprooted from its original setting to aggrandize Temple Newsam for, in a wider context, it is a defeat when such treasures leave their ancestral home. Leeds has invariably acted as a long-stop, often in concert with the Victoria and Albert Museum, to prevent pieces of national importance leaving the country when they appear on the art market.

Until about 1970 available funds were used almost exclusively to acquire aristocratic eighteenth century furniture because the finest interiors at Temple Newsam are of Georgian date. However, recently a move has been made to diversify the collection with interesting minor items such as a rare wrought-iron garden chair and a marbled stool based on one of C. H. Tatham's etchings, both dating from c.1800 and each one of a pair split with the Victoria and Albert Museum. A start has also been made on assembling anthologies of manuscript designs, samples of upholstery fabric, furniture trade catalogues and similar study material. As a result of organizing a series of exhibitions charting the regional character of seventeenth century oak furniture several richly carved pieces expressing local decorative traditions associated with Yorkshire, Lancashire and Cumbria have been bought. In addition space is shortly to be made available to harbour a range of ordinary backstairs furniture, Windsor chairs, cottage and farmhouse furniture and quite possibly pieces made for inns, schools, non-conformist chapels and similar products of the native vernacular tradition. Bringing together an enterprising range of common furniture will take time, but is a more logical development than the alternative strategy of fostering a continental collection.

Spending to improve the random holdings of Dutch and Flemish, French, Germanic and Italian furniture would hardly be justified, since elite (if mainly static) collections of European decorative art, which Leeds could never hope to match, already exist in this country. The great *bureau-plat* by Bernard II van Risenburgh, acquired in 1972 with the aid of a special government grant, was an exception because it is one of the few refined pieces of Louis XV furniture known to have been in England before the Seven Years War which ended in 1763. Furthermore, the fashionable architect designer John Vardy was moved to make an elegant pen and ink study of this Parisian table which may well prove to have a bearing on the emergence of the English rococo style. Since English furniture has always responded to influences from abroad the presence of some continental work is clearly relevant to the collection. Conversely, the modest quota of colonial furniture from Java, India and Ceylon based on English prototypes, helps to illuminate crosscurrents of taste. However, foreign furniture is likely always to remain a fringe element. The most significant alien holding is a collection of thirty-six Spanish Colonial pieces from Peru given by Lady Ramsden in 1955. At that date Temple Newsam could accommodate such exotic riches but a comparable offer might well pose a difficult problem today.

Lotherton Hall

The primary furniture collection at Temple Newsam has never been extended beyond the Regency period, an era formerly broadly accepted as dividing the age of hand craftsmanship from machine production. However, following an improved understanding of the nineteenth century furniture trade and the enhanced appreciation of Victorian decorative arts which emerged during the early 1960s this attitude became obsolete. The fact that, by long tradition, active collecting ceased around 1810 naturally generated frustration, for limitations of space at Temple Newsam precluded the acquisition of Victorian masterpieces. This apparently hopeless problem was unexpectedly resolved by an act of outstanding generosity when, in 1968, Sir Alvary and Lady Gascoigne presented Lotherton Hall near Aberford together with its garden and park, art treasures and, moreover, an endowment fund, to Leeds Corporation. Lotherton is a rambling, mainly late-Victorian country house possessing an intimate personality, complementary to but quite unlike the palatial character of Temple Newsam, ideal in fact to become a museum of nineteenth century and contemporary decorative art.

The Gascoigne furniture selected to form the nucleus of the permanent collection comes from many different sources. When the family vacated their ancestral home at nearby Parlington Hall in 1905 an auction sale was held, but the agent's marked catalogue records that numerous lots were bought-in and taken to Lotherton. Despite the dispersal of more pieces at a sale of surplus furnishings ordered in 1956 a significant residue of heirlooms traceable in the Parlington inventory of 1843 remains, including a large collection of documented furniture supplied to R.O. Gascoigne by Gillows of Lancaster in 1810–11. Certain items came from Himbleton Manor (the home of Sir Alvary's mother) while a late-Victorian davenport was previously at Waverley Abbey, the residence of Florence Nightingale who was related to the family. A group of sophisticated Chippendale and Sheraton Revival furniture associated with Edwards & Roberts of Oxford Street was purchased around 1880 by Lady Gascoigne's father Edmund Leatham of Wentbridge House, Yorkshire. A annotated inventory of Lotherton compiled in the 1930s reveals that other pieces in the collection were bought at local country house auctions including a pair of William and Mary style settees and two Italian chairs from the Temple Newsam sale of 1922. The Gascoignes, like Mrs. Meynell Ingram, regularly sailed to the continent aboard their yacht which explains the infiltration of several Dutch, French and Germanic items. Sir Alvary's father, who maintained close links with commonwealth countries and travelled extensively in the Orient, brought back a repertoire of furniture from South Africa, Korea and China which imparts a pleasantly individual flavour to the collection. Attention should also be drawn to an array of electric light fittings by Perry & Co. and other high class firms, installed when a generator was built at Lotherton about 1900, and to a fine range of artistic chimney furniture in the downstairs rooms.

Although Sir Alvary inherited Lotherton in 1937 the house in 1968 still reflected the eclectic Edwardian taste of his parents, for Sir Alvary's career in the diplomatic service kept him almost constantly abroad. A cross-section of this family accumulation was chosen to establish a basis for the permanent collection which is being steadily augmented by important Victorian treasures, often purchased with income from the endowment fund. Great care has been taken to seek furniture by eminent makers or designers, preferably of known date and with an accredited provenance. At the very first sale of Victorian furniture held by Christie's on 18 July 1968 Leeds secured a magnificent carved and painted oak wardrobe made about 1880 by Collier & Plucknett of Warwick for Tyntesfield and a documented corner dresser crafted at Ernest Gimson's Daneway Workshops in 1904. These two acquisitions established a high standard of artistic excellence. The collection now includes a remarkable octagonal marquetry table supplied by E. H. Baldock to the Duke of Buccleuch in 1840, two sumptuous dining chairs and a stool made to Pugin's design by Morel and Seddon for Windsor Castle in 1827–8 and an elegant amboyna writing table commissioned by Queen Victoria from Holland & Sons for Osborne House. A glamorous marble-topped centre table by William Burges, a unique papier-mâché bedroom suite manufactured in Birmingham, datable to 1851, a painted slate *dejune* table and several high-Victorian chairs by fashionable firms were amongst other early additions to the collection. Progressive designers such as C. L. Eastlake, E. G. Punnett, C. F. A. Voysey, Sir Edwin Lutyens, Ambrose Heal and Gordon Russell are also represented. However, the most outstanding single acquisition is unquestionably a lavish sycamore and marquetry bedroom suite comprising twelve separate items together with a grand piano and matching duet ottoman, all made in the 'Old English Style' by Marsh & Jones of Leeds to Charles Bevan's design for Titus Salt, Junior, of Milner Field, one of the wealthiest Yorkshire mill owners. This remarkable group, documented to 1865–6, compares favourably with the finest eighteenth century English furniture and is the subject of a special sub-section within the catalogue.

An adventurous, although logical extension of this collecting strategy has been the commissioning of modern wares for Lotherton, thus reviving the tradition of art patronage practiced by country house owners. John Hardy of Design Workshops, Huddersfield furnished the museum shop and oriental gallery, a lofty free-standing showcase for displaying contemporary pottery was bespoke from John Makepeace in 1976 and Roger Simpson has designed a pair of yew wood wall cases for modern jewellery. As a result of this enterprising policy Lotherton, in addition to providing an ideal setting for Victorian masterpieces, has become a home for the decorative arts of our own day.

The Catalogue

The fact that a piece of furniture is discussed in these volumes is no guarantee that it is of artistic importance, for the collection includes items that are not of the very highest quality. However, a complete catalogue is infinitely preferable to an anthology of what the author regards as relevant, because anyone who is engrossed in a subject develops unconscious prejudices. A catalogue is never light reading for its function is to record, as accurately and in as much detail as possible, all that is seriously worth recording about an object. This is not to imply that the end product is a mechanical inventory allowing no scope for personal value judgements for, by the thoroughness with which an entry has been prepared and attributes of prose style, one can express an opinion on the status of a piece. The verbal descriptions which form a vital ingredient may need some explanation since this cataloguing technique is frequently misunderstood. On the elementary level they convey essential data about construction and materials, compensate for the partial view and often misleading impression conveyed by photographs and help to forge an acceptable terminology for students of furniture. However, detailed descriptions perform an equally valuable non-academic function for, if the cataloguer is involved in a sustained creative act, a natural vitality or flatness of language betrays a personal response resulting in an individual statement, over and above the factual content, about each piece of furniture.

An important aspect of the cataloguer's job is to research and document works for the benefit of professional art historians, much as literary studies are underpinned and set on a firm footing by 'editorial' expertise and bibliographical scholarship. Accordingly, one of the most positive contributions is to identify the maker or designer and establish the date and provenance of furniture in the collection. In pursuit of this often elusive goal speculative attributions to particular firms have, on the whole, been avoided and a determined effort made to trace the origin of each object which, on occasion, has been rewarded by the discovery of a relevant bill or inventory. Additional information about many items will undoubtedly come to light and of course new pieces are constantly being acquired, so these volumes must be regarded as an interim report on the Leeds furniture collection.

Part One

ENGLISH FURNITURE

BAROMETERS

1 BAROMETER

By John Risso, Leeds
*c.*1805
Mahogany; rosewood

Of stick design; the mahogany trunk is crossbanded in rosewood and channelled to receive the exposed tube; the arched hood, enclosed by a glazed door framed between Doric columns, supports a moulded cresting set with turned brass finials; the mercury cistern is encased in a box faced as two dummy drawers with brass buckle-handles and a sliding lid. Original siphon tube with a pierced pear-shaped reservoir; the paired brass plates, marked with a scale measuring 28–31 in. subdivided into decimals and fitted with a manual vernier, are finely engraved with the Gascoigne crest 'a pike's head out of a ducal coronet' and a basket of flowers with seven weather indications for summer and winter conditions below at each side; signed across the bottom 'John Risso Fecit Leeds'.
H.102 (40).

One other stick barometer by John Risso has been recorded in Yorkshire.

PROV: R. O. Gascoigne, Parlington Hall, Yorkshire and by descent to Sir Alvary Gascoigne, Lotherton Hall; the Gascoigne gift 1968.   [7.175/68]

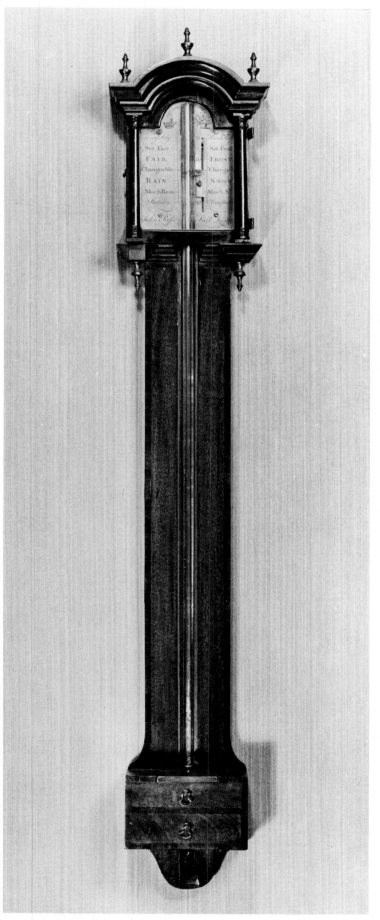

1

2 BAROMETER
By George and Charles Dixey, London
*c.*1830
Mahogany; ebony, box

Of bow-fronted stick design, the veneered trunk headed by a cove-moulded hood, terminates in an ebony vase-shaped cistern cover and the canted base is inlaid with ebony diamonds; the trunk is fronted by a mercury thermometer in its own glazed case with Fahrenheit and Reaumur scales on an ivory tablet. The tube rises from a leather based, turned boxwood mercury cistern with a portable screw below; the ivory plate is engraved with a scale measuring 27–31 in. simple weather indications and the maker's name 'G & C. Dixey / Opticians / to the KING / 3, New Bond St / LONDON'; the rack vernier is operated by a turned ivory knob set beneath the hood.
H.97 (38).

The twin brothers G. & C. Dixey were in partnership at 3 Bond Street, between 1825 and 1838. A barometer case of identical design is reproduced by N. P. Goodison, *English Barometers 1680–1860*, 1968, p.251, pl.154.

PROV: The Gascoigne family of Parlington Hall, Yorkshire; the Parlington sale (Hollis & Webb, Leeds) 24–29 July 1905, lot 6 (bought in); the Gascoigne gift 1968. [7.155/68]

BEDS

3 BED
*c.*1530
Oak

The heavily moulded tester is comprised of nine framed panels set with foliate rosettes and the frieze is richly carved with male and female masks amid acanthus scrolls with pierced valance boards designed as leafy dolphins separated by cherub masks; the built-in bedhead is constructed of ten panels arranged in three tiers; the top row, styled as architectural niches, centre on the arms of Wentworth (left) and Dronsfield (right) with a male and female bust carved in high-relief at either end; the middle row features a bold relief of St George on horseback slaying the dragon before a gothic castle with arcaded lateral panels representing David with his sling holding up the head of Goliath and Samson with the jaw-bone attacking a lion; the stiles are decorated with split columns and the rails with acanthus mouldings; the four bottom tablets bear portrait medallions and foliate diaper-work divided by guilloche uprights; the foot posts are formed of square pillars, the panelled sides embellished with engaged columns of scale and ribbed chain pattern; the upper vase and baluster-turned sections are richly carved with gadroons, acanthus fronds and fluting; the side rails carry pillow boards carved with grotesque heads.
H.244 (96); L.218 (86); W.173 (68).

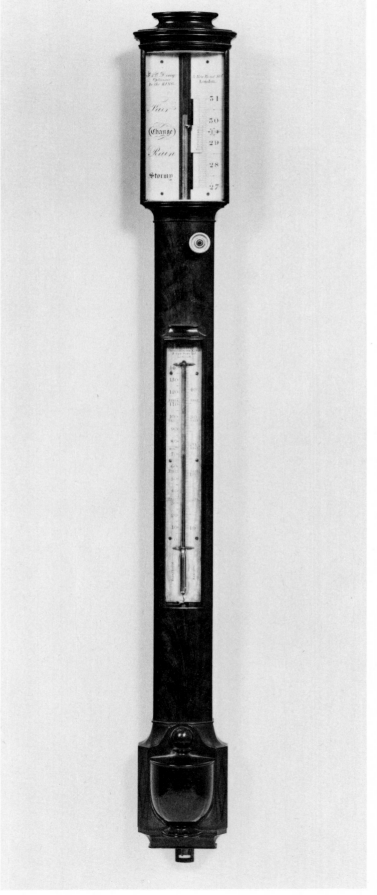

2

3

This bed has been rebuilt several times and although much of the cornice, base blocks, and rails are later additions and the bedhead betrays evidence of having been restructured the wealth of carved detail is of consistently good quality and the degree of restoration is acceptable in furniture of this early date.

A full account of the documentation relating to the bed together with a discussion of its stylistic character, the heraldic tablets, provenance and other information will be found under Cat. No.231 devoted to the companion dresser.

The words 'sent george' are visible in a badly torn portion of the inventory of Bretton taken in 1542 listing the contents of the room containing this bed. The St George relief and the two flanking panels were presumably based on contemporary woodcuts; no exact source has been found, but a popular woodcut printed in Delft, 1487, shows a very similar representation of St George slaying the dragon (M. J. Schretlen, *Dutch and Flemish Woodcuts of the Fifteenth Century*, 1925, pl.59).

The care taken by the Wentworth family to preserve this bed, despite regular domestic upheavals, underlines the extraordinary veneration in which State beds, particularly those with a Royal connection, were held. [4.6/47]

4 BED
*c.*1770
Mahogany; oak, pine

The richly carved and gilt cornices each centre on rococo shells crested by fruit and flower sprays and connected to tall acanthus plumes at each corner by scrolls styled informally with fronds, floral trails and an escalloped border; the coved tester is spanned by a shallow oval set with a foliate cross and eight radial leaf and husk spurs framed by anthemion spandrel motifs and a balanced design of C-scrolls and rococo elements, the whole composition being covered in damask; the turned and fluted footposts, each elaborated with a leafy baluster, gadrooned knop and enriched mouldings rest on square bases terminating in boldly knurled feet concealing large brass swivel castors with friction rollers; the bed bolts are masked by carved foliate tablets. The red silk damask hangings are lined with buckram interfacing and backed by calamanco; the scalloped valances and coverlet are trimmed with a knotted silk fringe headed by braided galons, the curtains and bases are edged with silk binding and the enriched tester is fully upholstered. The original material has been considerably rearranged during museum restoration and the curtains greatly reduced in width; the valance boards and drapes are annotated in ink, e.g. 'No 6 Inside'. Oak rails, headboard, stretchers and slats; the gilt cornice and tester pine; mahogany foot posts; continuous polished curtain rail.
H.305 (120); L.206 (81); W.183 (72).

The damask, patterned with broad conventional foliage and flowers with large petals and seed pods, is in 21 in. breadths with a repeat of 76 in. This basic design evolved in Genoa around 1730 and remained popular for several decades; a length is illustrated by P. K. Thornton, *Baroque and Rococo Silks*, 1965, fig.114A, but the existence of blue stripes in the selvedge suggests this fabric is English. A pair of window pelmets matching the cornices were acquired with the bed. The coverlet is of a later, differently patterned damask.

LIT: *Country Life*, 9 Nov. 1935, p.488, fig.7; G. Wills, *English Furniture 1760–1900*, 1971, p.15, repr. (colour).

PROV: Acquired by a member of the Darley family of Aldby Hall, Yorkshire during the last century, reputedly from one of the Gascoigne's country houses near Aberford; bought from Colonel G. Darley 1959. [15/59]

5 BED
Probably by B. Evans, London
*c.*1825
Mahogany; beech, pine

The cornices of scrolled-pediment design centre on tall carved and pierced acanthus plumes with elaborate anthemion fans below; the long S-scrolls have acanthus sheath and rosette terminals; the turned and cabled front pillars are supported on square panelled bases enriched with anthemia and headed by leafy faceted balusters between collars of guilloche and gadrooning; turned stump feet banded with lotus; the framed foot and headboards are crested by paired scrolls enriched with tendrils and seeded foliage, the central volutes supporting anthemion bunches. The back posts, canopy-ribs and underframing are of beech; pine top-rails, cornice boards and slats; the bed bolts are masked by sliding panels; polished iron curtain rail, the cornices braced by a skeleton of iron struts. A length of the original material (26 × 70 in.) has been removed from behind the headboard, a block-printed cotton figuring an arborescent design in gold on a red ground with a 9½ in. repeat; the original cotton lining (also on the headboard) displays a red-dotted vermiculate pattern. The present white cotton fabric is roller printed in reds, blues, greens, yellows and sepia with an overall design of lanterns, exotic birds and insects, baskets of fruit and flowering boughs in the Chinese taste, carrying a repeat of 26 in. The festooned headcloth and valances are edged with a wool bullion fringe; slightly arched tester cloth, plain inner valance, padded head and foot panels, gathered bases; the original set of curtains extended around the foot, the present chintz hangings draw only halfway along each side.
H.351 (138); L.213 (84); W.183 (72).

One of the cornice backboards is inscribed 'H. Simpson, Joiner, Cliffton Castle, March 24 1896' and a couch upholstered *en suite* (Cat. No.330) is signed in pencil 'Jn Page, Upholster, York Dec'r 7th 1880' which presumably indicates the date of the present hangings.

Three window pelmets matching the cornices with curtains *en suite* were acquired with the bed; each unit consists of three mahogany components secured by bolts to pine backboards and the various parts bear numbered cards to ensure correct assembly and positioning within the room, e.g. 'East Window No.1' or 'Right Hand Window'. The eleven inscribed tags are made from two cut-up trade

4

5

cards (both incomplete) one issued by 'B. EVANS / CABINET MAKER / 3, WHEATSHEAF YARD' who advertised pedestal sideboards, telescopic dining-tables, loo, sofa and card tables, sofa and socket bedsteads etc., the other belonging to a Southwark dealer in tortoiseshell and minerals. Nothing is known of B. Evans apart from an entry in Robson's *Directory*, 1826, recording a cabinet maker of this name at 5, Clerkenwell Green. The bed is much more spectacular than the furniture Gillows supplied to Clifton Castle between 1809 and 1818, although it relates to a richly carved and gilt overmantel mirror still in the house; both pieces can be roughly dated from stylistic affinities with ornamental designs in P. and M. A. Nicholson's *Practical Cabinet-Maker*, 1826.

LIT: C. G. Gilbert, *L. G. & R. F.*, 1972, p.57, repr.

PROV: By descent from Timothy Hutton of Clifton Castle, Masham, Yorkshire to Mrs. J. H. Curzon-Herrick who gave the bed to Leeds 1963.   [23/63]

5

6 BEDHEAD
19th century, first quarter
Oak; pine

The chamfered corner posts are united by three cross rails framing two tiers of panels headed by a short tester banded along each side with guilloche and fronted by an oak rail inscribed 'THYS BED TOO REYMAYEN FOR EVER' in gothic script. The lowest cross-member on the bedhead is a narrow board inlaid with matched compositions of spiralling leafy stems and ball flowers issuing from a mound executed in light and dark woods; the strip has been reduced at each end and fixed upside down. The bottom row of three panels centres on an heraldic shield displaying 'ary on a bend sable three eagles' (Popeley) impaling 'three pales sable on a bend gules three mullets or' (Dronsfield) set between lozenge panels enclosing male and female profile heads, the stiles are enriched with a foliated zig-zag and the cross-rail, which has been reduced, is carved with a vine-trail issuing from a bold lion's mask. The upper stage centres on addorsed satyrs playing pipes carved in high relief flanked by roundels containing a female head and the arms of Dronsfield, with pilasters in the form of male therms supported on lion's-mask plinths and headed by vases of flowers; the frieze decorated with vines, has been amputated from the medial rail.
H.180 (71); W.112 (44).

An old photograph shows the bed with a corded canvas bottom, plain side bars and a simple footboard outlined with an applied guilloche panel set between short chamfered posts. The bedhead has been built up from old components framed by nineteenth century posts and cross ties. The five panels are contemporary with and attributable to the same school as the woodwork from the Henry VIII room at Bretton Hall (Cat. Nos.3 and 231); the sectioned vine-trail rail and figures are probably Elizabethan, the inlaid board appears to be slightly later. Some carved details such as vestigial bird heads reflect local decorative traditions. The canopy of pine faced with oak is likely to date from the early nineteenth century.

The antiquarian Joseph Hunter includes a rather am-

5

biguous description of this bed in his *South Yorkshire*, 1831, Vol.II, p.249. Some of the features he records are recognizable, but others must refer to the second historic bed at Bretton (Cat. No.3).

'A very ancient bed is still preserved at Bretton-hall; it has the arms of Dronsfield, on a panel between two other pannels, on which are carved the head of a male figure, with curled hair and a piked beard, and the head of a female figure with a necklace, and the cap put far back on the head. Above is carved in black letters THYS BED TO REMAYEN FOR EVER. Among other carved work about this bed is St George killing the dragon . . .'

The above passage provides acceptable evidence that the bedhead is a very early example of the fashion for antiquarian oak furniture.

LIT: A. Oswald, 'Woodwork at Bretton', *Country Life*, 9 July 1938, p. xxxviii, fig.2; *L.A.C.*, No.2 (1947) p.8, repr.

PROV: The Wentworths of Bretton Hall, Wakefield, Yorkshire; given by Viscount Allendale 1947.   [4.7/47]

BED, papier-mâché
*c.*1851, Birmingham
Under Cat. No.515 (illustrated)

7 BED
Late 19th century
Oak; walnut

Turned posts with square bases centering on a cup and cover formation with fluted, reeded, stiff-leaf and stamped decoration, the rails united to the uprights by bolts; the headboard is constructed of three arcaded panels surmounted by a gadrooned shelf backed by two arched panels carved with vases of sprawling foliage flanked by pilasters in the form of Elizabethan terminal figures; the top rail embellished with grotesque masks and dragons; the tester is composed of twelve framed panels incised with simply styled lozenge motifs bordered by a gadrooned cornice; iron curtain rod; the brass castors marked 'AUTO CASTOR & WHEEL Co Ltd / LONDON PATENT 1895'. Oak, some old wood re-used in the tester, with walnut posts.
H.224 (88); L.201 (79); W.127 (50).

PROV: Probably bought by the Hon. Mrs. E. C. Meynell Ingram who attempted to re-create the baronial character of Temple Newsam during the last quarter of the nineteenth century; purchased at the Temple Newsam sale (Robinson, Fisher & Harding) 26–31 July, 1922, lot 209.
[1922/F43]

6

6

8 TWIN BEDS
By Heal & Sons, London
*c.*1903
Mahogany; satinwood, oak

The bedheads are of rectangular design with square posts and an open double-X lattice system framed between the flat moulded top rails and base boards; decorated with satinwood strings, crossbanding and insets. The lower footboards are of matching pattern. The posts are fitted with cast brackets into which an iron frame supporting a grid of interlacing straps slots. Oak cross-rails, brass castors with pottery wheels. The sprung mattresses fold in three sections.
H.129 (51); L.198 (78); W.101 (40).

The mattresses are labelled 'HEAL & SONS PATENT / Bedstead, Bedding and Bedroom Furniture / Manufactory / 195, 196, 197 & 198 Tottenham Court Rd., / LONDON'. This model was illustrated in the firm's *Catalogue of Bedsteads, Bedding, Blankets, Sheets & Down Quilts*, April 1903, p.90, No.120 'Sheraton' style £7.0.0. There was formerly a doubled bed *en suite*.

PROV: Lotherton Hall; the Gascoigne gift 1971.   [23.23/71]

8

BOOKCASES

9 BOOKCASE
*c.*1765
Mahogany; oak, pine

The breakfront cabinet is constructed of four upright units raised on a low plinth and surmounted by a broken pediment centering on a platform; the cornice is enriched with dentils and a simple gothic fret. Each section is fronted by a solid cupboard door outlined with an astragal panel while the upper stage, fitted with adjustable shelves, is enclosed by doors fronted with gothic-pattern glazing bars composed of two tiers of tracery headed by cusped and pointed arches. The doors are mounted with flush brass bolts and ornamental escutcheons; the lower wing doors were originally secured by a peg and slot catch operated from above. Panelled oak back, sides and shelves; pine plinth and cornice with mahogany facings.
H.259 (102); W.292 (105); D.41 (16½).

The pattern of glazing bars is a simplified version of a design for a Library Bookcase in Thomas Chippendale's *Director*, 1762, pl. xcvii, while the pediment is related to a model shown on pl. xci and the cupboard doors resemble those on an example illustrated as pl.lxxxvii. The piece is similar, but much inferior, to a bookcase at Nostell Priory which can be associated with a payment to Chippendale dated 23 June 1766.

PROV: By descent from C. A. Goodricke of Ilkley, Yorkshire to the Rev. Guy A. Goodricke; given by him 1955. [10/55]

10 BOOKCASE
*c.*1765
Mahogany; pine

Of breakfront design fitted with adjustable shelves; the upper stage consists of a central cupboard enclosed by double doors flanked by narrower wings, the open pediment, centering on a plinth for a bust, and the cornice are enriched with dentils and gothic blocking, the moulded glazing bars form an interlocking pattern of octagons and rectangles, originally backed by green silk curtains; the lower stage, containing three shelved cupboards with fielded panel doors, is headed by a moulded rail and rests on a solid plinth. Flush brass door bolts and locks, the drop handle is a later addition; pine carcase, solid mahogany doors and ends, veneered tympanum, the shelves, partitions and cresting faced with mahogany.
H.290 (114); W.295 (116); D.56 (22).

The overall design and glazing bars are closely related to a library bookcase in Chippendale's *Director* (1754) pl.lxiii.

PROV: The Gascoignes of Parlington Hall, Yorkshire; removed to Lotherton Hall about 1905; the Gascoigne gift 1968.   [7.168/68]

11 BOOKCASE
18th century, last quarter
Mahogany; oak, pine

Built in two stages divided by a narrow shelf; the upper part is fitted with adjustable shelves enclosed by double doors fronted by a conventional pattern of octagonal and rectangular glazing bars; dentil cornice with a platform behind to support library busts. The lower section contains cupboards enclosed by double doors each faced as a pair of panels outlined with fillets; plain plinth. The doors are fitted with flush brass bolts and locks.
H.257 (101); W.183 (72); D.56 (22).

PROV: The Gascoignes of Parlington Hall, Yorkshire; removed to Lotherton Hall about 1905; the Gascoigne gift 1968.
[7.167/68]

12 BOOKCASE
c.1790
Mahogany; pine

Of breakfront design with a plain frieze and dentil cornice; the upper stage, built as a single unit, consists of a central section flanked by narrower wings, each part being enclosed by a tall door fitted with panes of crown glass supported by slender gothic-pattern astragals; the lower stage, headed by a small ledge and set on a plain plinth, contains three cupboards with panelled doors veneered in figured mahogany outlined with a simple string and crossbanded borders. The sides are grooved for adjustable shelves and the pine interior is stained red, thread escutcheons.
H.277 (109); W.221 (87); D.46 (18).

PROV: Removed by the Earl and Countess of Chesterfield

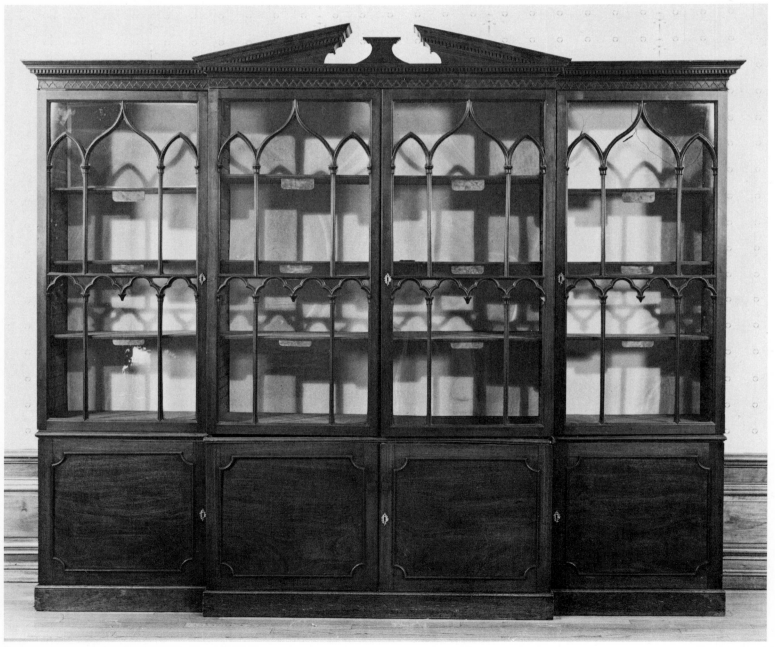

from Holme Lacy, Herefordshire to Beningbrough Hall, Yorkshire; W. F. Greenwood & Sons; bought 1943. [1/43]

13 BOOKCASE
*c.*1800 (outer wings later)
Mahogany and rosewood; oak, pine, elm

Of double breakfront design headed by a dentil cornice; the upper stage consists of five separate units – a central cabinet enclosed by double doors flanked by narrower cupboards and side wings, the doors are veneered in rosewood and filled with crown glass set in octagonal glazing bars; grooved for adjustable bookshelves. The lower part is in three sections – a central cupboard enclosing four large drawers with integral wings (once containing pairs of drawers, now gutted) and detached wings at each end providing shelved compartments. The doors are fronted by recessed octagonal panels in mahogany outlined by a chequered string and framed in a crossbanded rosewood surround; the dividing ledge is veneered with bordered panels of mahogany; original brass door bolts and half-round flush drawer handles set in circular plates, later door handles and locks. The central bookcase has oak sides, a pine top, back, base, shelves and drawers with elm partitions in the lower stage.
H.251 (99); W.411 (162); D.57 (22½).

The existence of a dentil cornice on the returns of the central section, structural differences and the evidence of timber prove that the lateral wings were added to the older

10

bookcase. Although very carefully styled to match the original part the plank backboards suggest a Victorian date. The left cupboard bears a label inscribed 'Est. 1870 / Fred Martin / French Polisher / St Andrew Gate / York / 1920'.

PROV: Lord Brotherton, Kirkham Abbey, Yorkshire, who may have acquired it from the previous owner Lord Liverpool; given by Mrs. A. Myddleton 1967. [26/67]

TWO BOOKCASES, mahogany
By Gillows, Lancaster, 1811
Under Cat. No.539 (illustrated)

14 BOOKCASE
Early 19th century
Mahogany; pine

Of breakfront design with a moulded cornice; the upper stage which is in three sections, the central part slightly taller than the wings, is enclosed by doors with a conventional geometrical glazing pattern and contains adjustable shelves supported on turned wooden pegs; the lower part constructed as a single unit, contains four long and eight short graduated drawers, some with internal divisions. Flush brass door bolts, thread escutcheons and brass knobs ornamented with a sunk rosette. Solid mahogany sides and door frames, pine carcase and drawers, veneered front, inner surfaces stained pink. The underside of one long drawer roughly incised '1047'.
H.234 (92); W.208 (82); D.43 (17).

PROV: Bequeathed by Mrs. Frank Gott, Weetwood Garth, Leeds 1941. [7.19/41]

15 BOOKSHELVES
19th century, first half
Oak; pine

The lower stage which consists of three open shelves is surmounted by a panelled rear structure, both sections being largely built from fragments of seventeenth century woodwork. The top part frames two recessed panels each inlaid with an identical formalized plant design having leafy tendrils bearing globe flowers executed in light and dark elements. The panels are set in enriched mouldings framed by a guilloche crest rail, a base rail carved with gadrooned lunettes and the stiles are faced with male and female therms, a narrow shelf extends across the top. The lower stage provides three open bookshelves with lozenge end panels, a central division and fluted frieze; the openings were originally headed by red leather valances. The left-hand pilaster is fashioned as a female therm above a lion's mask suspending a fruit swag ending in a tassel and drapery; the central division is fronted by a male therm above a cherub-head console and beribboned fruit swag, while the right-hand pilaster is carved as a male therm above a long acanthus frond. The twin baseboards set between split spiral columns are enriched with dragon-scrolls on a punched ground, the central block bears a tiny sunk medallion featuring an

13

heraldic bird with an arrow through its head; pine back-boards.
H.173 (68); W.152 (60); D.35 (14).

The structure is almost wholly built of old timber, the top section may once have been a bedhead or overmantel but the lower part is a pastiche of antique fragments, even the shelves being sawn-up panelling. The carved work displays no coherent regional content. The valanced leather frill possesses a Regency flavour. Compare Cat. Nos.6 and 235.

PROV: The Wentworths of Bretton Hall, Wakefield, York-shire; given by Viscount Allendale 1947.   [4.4/47]

16 BOOKCASE
Late 19th century
Mahogany; pine, oak

Of upright rectangular design surmounted by a broken pediment with dentil enrichment centering on a platform; fronted by tall double doors, the upper part glazed with

15

bevelled panes, the lower part enclosed by fielded panels; ornamented with egg and dart, and ribbon and rosette mouldings; four shelves within; brass bolts and escutcheons. Solid mahogany with a panelled pine back, oak base, top and shelves.
H.259 (102); W.122 (48); D.43 (17).

The cornice and pediment have been added, probably about 1900, to what appears to be a late Victorian bookcase in the early Georgian style. An old acquisitions register states that the cabinet is stamped 'GILLOWS LONDON AND LANCASTER'; the mark could have been lost when the shelves were altered for display purposes.

PROV: W. D. Cutter, Great Russell St., London; Sotheby's, 16 May 1924, lot 479; M. Harris & Sons; bought 1943.
[2/43]

BOOT-JACK

17 BOOT-JACK
Possibly by Gillows, Lancaster
*c.*1820
Mahogany

The platform base has a U-shaped slot-and-spur socket at one end, with reeded standards at each side headed by a turned cross-bar handle, a central slat swings on a pivot between the posts; mahogany with brass furrules.
H.80 (31½).

This gadget was designed to aid the removal of top-boots, the heel being inserted and gripped in the slot and the arm tilted to press down on the toe, assisting leverage. Closely similar models were made by Gillows of Lancaster during the Regency period.

PROV: Cooper & Launder (Antiques), Wakefield; bought 1957.
[19/57]

BOXES

18 BOX
17th century, second half
Oak

Of plank construction, united by nails, the front board is carved with two panels of scrolling auricular design on a stippled ground and has scalloped corners; tapered side battens under the lid (one replaced in mahogany) bored to receive integral wooden tongue hinges; iron hasp and lock plate not original, later end handles removed. An ancient label pasted inside reads 'Old Linen & Calico bandages'.
H.28 (11); W.65 (25½); D.33 (13).

The fleshy scroll enrichment relates to carving found on chairs and fixed woodwork in Yorkshire. A chair at Conisbrough church (*Oak Furniture From Yorkshire Churches*, Temple Newsam, Exh. Cat. 1971 (28) repr.) and another at Burton Constable (*Country Life*, 27 Aug. 1937, p.243, fig.13) feature almost identical panels; there are allied examples at Bolton Percy church and Fountains Hall and pews in Bramhope church, consecrated 1649, are similarly styled. The chest expresses a strong regional character.

PROV: Private collection in Beverley, East Yorkshire; M. Goldstone & Son; bought 1973.
[22/73]

17

18

19 DRESSING BOX
*c.*1670
Beech and tortoiseshell

Of casket form with a domed top; the exterior is veneered with tortoiseshell tinted red and set with brass mounts; the corner mounts are engraved with stylized roses, the oval lockplate with an oak wreath and the lid, outlined with a moulded panel, centres on a lozenge escutcheon and loop handle; the interior, lined with pink satin and galoon strips, has a mirror in the lid and a slip box which lifts out to reveal a glass panelled well, the bottom decorated with a water-colour painting of Charles II and his family seated at a table in a garden (after an engraving by Abraham Bosse titled *Manhood*). The composition is intended to be viewed in the reflection of the under-lid mirror which also captures an image of the inside front panel painted with figures in a park surveying an ornamental pool formed by a mirror panel;

the silvered key handle incorporates a double 'C' monogram surmounted by the Royal crown.
H.16.5 (6½); W.35.5 (14); D.24 (9½).

PROV: The underside of the slip box is stencilled 'D.U.R.' for Dorothy Una Ratcliffe the pen name of Mrs. D. U. McGrigor Phillips; given by her niece Miss Ludmila Mlada 1968. [6.5/68]

20 WORKBOX ON STAND
*c.*1795
Satinwood; burr yew, sycamore, mahogany, pine

Rectangular box with bevelled lid and a drawer in the base; the top and sides are inset with oval panels of burr yew and banded with geometric inlay between strings; the stand has

19

slender, tapering legs terminating in brass collars and diagonal stretchers centering on a small oval plaque; the frieze is bordered and decorated with corner medallions; the drawer (formerly partitioned) and box are lined with quilted plush overlaying the original pink paper, both are fitted with locks. Pine carcase veneered with satinwood and embellished with various figured, green-stained and natural woods; the stand has a mahogany platform and rails with satinwood veneer and solid legs.
H.89 (35); W.28 (11); D.21 (8¼).

Mount marks show that the end panels were fitted with oval handles and deep sockets each side of the lid indicate that the box was also provided with an arched strap handle comparable to one on a workbox and stand of similar design illustrated by P. Macquoid, *The Age of Satinwood*, 1908, pl. xiv.

LIT: C. G. Gilbert, *L. G. & R. F.* 1972, p.4, repr.

PROV: Given by Frank H. Fulford 1939.   [9.51/39]

21 WORKBOX ON STAND
*c.*1810
Rosewood; mahogany, pine, sycamore

The octagonal box containing three shallow trays of uniform depth, is raised on four tapering flared legs joined by curved stretchers of ply construction; the hinged lid is decorated with a worn coloured print representing Ariadne standing in a chariot drawn by a lion with her dog running alongside; the box is bordered with chevron bands between multiple strings in various natural and green-stained woods; ivory diamond escutcheon. Pine carcase and legs veneered with rosewood, sycamore edge facings and box corner strings; mahogany trays; the interior lined with grey plush and stippled paper. Roman joint numerals I-IV.
H.75 (29½); Diam. 36 (14¼).

PROV: Given by Frank H. Fulford 1939.   [9.53/39]

20

21

BRACKETS

22 CORNER BRACKET
*c.*1730–40
Pine

The triangular shelf with a shaped fore-edge is supported
underneath by a broken scroll styled with a twisted ribbon
moulding, panelled sides and fronded volutes, oak leaf and
acorn cluster pendant. The top is unlikely to be original.
H.41 (16½).

22

23

23 WALL-BRACKET
*c.*1745
Pine

Of semi-circular form with a gadrooned platform, the vase-shaped body is boldly carved with acanthus foliage and at the base a bead-ribbed frond curls over a short stalk, broken at the end. A bracket of strikingly similar design illustrated in *D.E.F.*, I, p.117, fig.4 indicates that the pendant originally terminated in a second frond bearing a cluster of fruit and flowers. Traces of a white ground coating show that the surface was once painted.
H.36 (14¼); W.26 (10½).

Stylistic affinities with the chimneypieces, supplied by Richard Fisher of York for new interiors created on the west wing at Temple Newsam between *c.*1738 and 1745, suggest he may have carved this bracket. Possibly recorded in the Temple Newsam inventory of 1808 'Lady Irwins Bed Chamber – a carved bracket'.

EXH: *Temple Newsam Heirlooms*, 1972 (27).

PROV: The Ingrams of Temple Newsam; given by the Earl of Halifax 1922. [1922/F15]

24 CORNER BRACKET
19th century, second half
Oak

The triangular platform with a lobed and moulded front is supported on a scrolled canopy, while the recessed lower part centres on the head of a jester wearing a cowl with tassel and bells carved in high relief bordered by garlands of flowers and fruit. The block carved with a head dates from the medieval period, the oak grain being much more open and weathered than the timber used for the Victorian garlands, canopy and platform. The old fragment has been very skilfully incorporated.
H.31 (12½); D.23 (9).

This fine specimen of antiquarian oak furniture can be associated with Mrs E. C. Meynell Ingram's improvements at Temple Newsam which included the construction of a super-Jacobethan staircase.

PROV: The Hon. Mrs E. C. Meynell Ingram of Temple Newsam; given by the Earl of Halifax 1922. [1922/F48]

24

25

drawers and the central door is missing; oak carcase, rosewood drawer linings.
H.135 (53); W.107 (42½); D.39 (15½).

PROV: Bought from H. Blairman & Sons, who contributed half the cost 1945.   [21.1/45]

BUREAUX

Writing Cabinets, Scriptor, Secretaires etc.

25 SCRIPTOR
Late 17th century (modified)
Lignum vitae; oak, pine, rosewood

The upper stage, fitted with a fall front beneath two drawers, is fully veneered with an octagonal pattern of lignum vitae parquetry outlined by half-round mouldings; the stand has spirally-turned corner supports ending in bun feet, the moulded frieze rails and flat stretcher being faced with parquetry; the fall front opens on lopers to reveal a leather writing panel backed by a façade of small drawers and pigeon holes around a large central compartment originally enclosed by a door. The amorini cartouche-pattern escutcheons are reproduction. The pine stand with a plank top appears to be modern, the lack of lower frieze drawers, stretcher pattern and side ledges being untypical of the period; although refinished the upper stage is more convincing, however, several of the slots originally contained

26 BUREAU-CABINET
By John Gatehouse, London
c.1705
Walnut; oak, pine

The upper stage has a straight moulded cornice and is enclosed by double doors, each faced with a raised panel of figured walnut outlined by feathered crossbanding and a moulded surround; the doors are backed by oak boards corresponding to the shaped front panels. The interior contains two adjustable shelves above a central niche flanked by letter holes and drawers; the cupboard base incorporates two candle slides. The lower part is bordered by half-round mouldings and veneered with figured walnut, the slope and drawers being styled with feathered crossbanding. The desk opens on lopers to reveal a small central cupboard between rows of letter holes with ogee openings above shallow drawers, one of which contains the maker's label; the bun feet have been renewed. Original locks, hinges and engraved brass key escutcheons, the loop drawer handles and oval lock plates are of a pattern current about 1790. The upper stage

has an oak carcase, the lower part, pine sides and inner structures.
H.201 (79); W.101 (40); D.59 (23).

The label of John Gatehouse, a previously unrecorded London maker, reads 'JOHN GATEHOUSE, Cabinet Maker / at the *Golden-Ball* by the *Ditch-Side*, near / *Holbourn-Bridge London* Maketh and Selleth all / Sorts of Cabinet Work, Chests of Drawers, / Book-Cases, Cabinets, Scrutores; All Sorts of / Glasses, Pier-Glasses, Chimney-Glasses and Scon / ces; Also all Sorts of Joiners-Work; as Oval- / Tables, &c. At reasonable Rates'.

An old cloth tab attached to the bunch of keys is inscribed 'Jervoise Esq / 705 / Queen Anne / Bureau Bookcase'. *

PROV: Herriard Park, Hampshire, built by Thomas Jervoise in 1704 and by descent to Major F. H. T. Jervoise (d.1959); inherited by H. B. Powell, Farrington Hurst, Hampshire, who demolished the house; allocated to Leeds City Council by H.M. Treasury in satisfaction of estate duty 1976. [32/76]

27 BUREAU WRITING AND DRESSING TABLE
(originally surmounted by a mirror, the stand later)
*c.*1720
Hawthorn (?) and walnut; oak, pine, sycamore

In the form of a small desk with flat top, slope front and a drawer under, veneered with 'moss-agate' parquetry outlined with string borders, crossbanded and chequered surrounds. The hinged flap rests, when open, on lopers and provides a leather writing surface backed by thirteen small drawers and four letter holes centering on a cupboard enclosing three small drawers, some partitioned and fitted with concealed compartments; the interior is veneered in figured walnut inset with strings. The rectangular stand, raised on straight chamfered legs with fretted brackets, and the frieze, ornamented with gilt mouldings and applied rococo foliage, probably dates from about 1740; slots in the top indicate that the desk was originally surmounted by standards supporting a swing toilet glass. Oak top, drawer linings and inner door; pine bottom, flap, back, some internal divisions and stand rails; walnut sides, letter holes and legs; sycamore

26

27

leather top are recent. A piece of red lining leather under the right-hand ink drawer is clearly original.
H.90 (35½); W.72 (28¼); D.49 (19½).

Walnut furniture of traditional form was produced in provincial workshops up to 1750 and even later.

PROV: By descent to the Hon. Mrs Fairfax, Acomb House, York; the Fairfax sale (Lawson, Maskell & Giddings, York) 22–23 Feb. 1961, lot 194; bequeathed by Sir George Martin 1976.   [51.31/76]

28

strings; brass-hinges, drawer pulls and pierced escutcheons.
H.106 (42); W.74 (29); D.51 (20).

The unusual parquetry veneer has either been cut from a log attacked by fungus or is one of the rare timbers with a dark heart and light sapwood such as laburnum, blackthorn or hawthorn. A bureau veneered with similar parquetry is illustrated *D.E.F.*, I, p.130, fig.17.

PROV: One of the secret drawers contains a printed card inscribed 'Pierre Leandri' and the back bears the label of an Edinburgh furniture depository; bought from H. C. Foot (Antiques) with the aid of a government grant 1946.
[9.1/46]

28 BUREAU
*c.*1730–40
Walnut; pine, oak

Of pedestal design with a fall-front desk drawer and leather top; the partitioned interior centres on a small cupboard flanked by pairs of shallow drawers and letter holes while each pedestal contains three drawers with moulded edges faced by boxwood string panels; the internal surfaces and knee-hole cupboard, which is headed by an ogee rail, are similarly outlined; raised on square bracket feet. When shut the fall flap is held in an upright position by brass hooks and eyes. Pine carcase with oak drawers, the escutcheons and

29 WRITING CABINET
*c.*1745
Mahogany; oak, pine, sycamore

The lower stage, raised on shaped bracket feet, consists of a serpentine-fronted commode with reeded corners containing four long and eight short graduated drawers with moulded edges; the top drawer is partitioned and accommodates a hinged writing flap backed by a horse, the surface covered with tooled and gilt brown leather; the cabinet stage, enclosed by double doors, is of architectural design with fluted and cabled pilasters headed by Ionic capitals, blocks and a pulvinated leaf-frieze surmounted by a broken pediment enriched with dentils between egg and dart and acanthus mouldings; the central break features a plinth and the base contains three revealed flanked by two concealed drawers with panelled fronts below a gadrooned moulding; inside the main doors are styled with panels set in shaped frames; the interior contains a central fall-front desk flanked by tiers of drawers faced as shallow niches and surmounted by twenty-four block-fronted alphabet drawers with shelves

29

mahogany; pine bottom, the alphabet insets and marquetry detail are in sycamore.
H.269 (106); W.158 (62½); D.76 (30).

Three other bureau cabinets of strikingly similar countenance, scale and internal design have been recorded, the main variant features being a display of rococo carving on the main doors of two examples with an Irish provenance (Castletown, Co. Kildare – *Country Life*, 18 July 1936, p.73 and Castlewellan, Co. Down – *Apollo*, Oct. 1966, p.285) and an alternative form of swan-neck pediment (Burton Park, Sussex – *Country Life*, 18 July 1936, p.72). The parallels of design, particularly in the elaborate internal fitments and coincidence of archaic seaweed marquetry lunettes suggest this group was built by the same, possibly Irish, firm of cabinet-makers. A minority school of opinion favours associating these pieces with Gillows of Lancaster who were well-placed to export furniture to Ireland.

LIT: *Apollo*, Dec. 1941, p.142, repr.; *Antique Collector*, Dec. 1958, p.239, fig.3; F. Lewis Hinckley, *Directory of Queen Anne, Early Georgian and Chippendale Furniture*, 1971, pl.100.

PROV: Given by Mrs Frank Tugwell of Scarborough in memory of her husband 1940.   [10/40]

for folio volumes above; the writing flap, inset with a shapely fielded panel opens on lopers to reveal a small central cupboard surrounded by alphabet letter holes with shelves below; the door, set between pilasters that slide forward as secret compartments, encloses two small drawers and there is a third behind the seaweed marquetry lunette above. The brass escutcheons replace an earlier set of single socket handles; the main doors hang on three strap hinges and are secured with brass bolts; the inner drawers have turned ivory pulls; brass locks. Veneered mahogany front, the carved features and sides solid mahogany; oak backboards and drawer linings; the top, bottom, internal divisions and drawer fronts of the commode are pine; the cupboard interior is of oak faced with mahogany, the double doors and desk flap of framed panel construction are also

30

30 BUREAU
*c.*1745–50
Walnut; pine, oak

Veneered in walnut, the top, hinged-flap and cock-beaded drawers crossbanded and outlined with feathered string panels; the writing interior is also veneered and fitted with three shallow drawers above a row of six letter holes; raised on square bracket feet. The two short drawers are constructed of pine while the long drawers are of oak with pine backboards, all contain old blue lining paper. Pine carcase, oak lopers, escutcheons not original.
H.94 (37); W.76 (30); D.43 (17).

Robert Williams has drawn my attention to a closely similar walnut bureau (recently in the trade) by a Suffolk cabinet maker inscribed with the date 1749. Cat. No.30 is a piece of comparable provincial quality.

PROV: By descent to Colonel William Warde-Aldham, Hooton Pagnell Hall, Doncaster, Yorkshire; sold about 1930; bequeathed by Sir George Martin 1976. [51.23/76]

31

32

31 DESK AND BOOKCASE
*c.*1795
Birch; rosewood, satinwood, oak, pine, mahogany

Built in three sections held in position by register pegs; the upper stage with tray top and two drawers below, contains an adjustable bookshelf enclosed by double doors framing mirror plates; various scars indicate the doors were originally glazed with a diagonal pattern of bars backed by panels of pleated silk. The cylinder-front writing flap opens to reveal a desk fitted with small drawers and letter holes; veneer grafts (confirmed by removal of the back) show that the desk was originally closed by a ?tambour shutter with writing slide below, and the existing front, incorporating a shallow document well, has been constructed at a later date. The lower stage containing one long and two short drawers

is raised on square tapered legs with inlaid strings; the feet have been shortened by about two inches. Veneered in birch crossbanded with rosewood, inner structures oak and pine except for the cylinder front which is built of mahogany staves; satinwood legs, turned rosewood knobs, and brass stays supporting the fall-front. The central drawer is stencilled '17431' underneath.
H.165 (65); W.87 (34½); D.52 (20½).

Based on a design dated 1792 for a 'Cylinder Desk and Bookcase' in Thomas Sheraton's *Drawing-Book*, pl.47. He states 'The style is somewhat elegant, being made of satinwood crossbanded and varnished. This design shows green silk fluting behind the glass . . . the square figure of the door is much in fashion now.'

PROV: A subscription form issued by the Invalids' Kitchen, Leeds in 1869 and bearing the name 'Mrs Lupton, The Harehills' (found in a rear cavity) indicates that this piece passed by descent to Agnes and Norman Lupton who bequeathed it to Leeds 1953.   [13.381/53]

32 SECRETARY AND BOOKCASE
c.1800
Mahogany; pine, oak

In two stages, the upper part surmounted by a moulded cornice and enclosed by double doors with glazing bars of gothic design, pierced brass pegs prove the doors were backed by pleated silk; the sides grooved for book shelves with reeded fronts. The lower stage contains a fall-front desk with three graduated drawers below, raised on square bracket feet united by aprons; the secretaire provides a baize-covered writing surface with quadrant supports, internal letter holes, small drawers with turned ivory pulls and two narrow document compartments disguised as book spines (Gray's Poems, Vols.1 & 2 in red tooled and gilt leather). Solid mahogany sides and doors, carcase and inner structures pine apart from secretary fitments which are of oak; the lower drawers pine with veneered fronts and cock beads, exposed pine surfaces stained red. Brass door beading, bolts and quadrants with spring-catch release, steel drawer locks, the bronze handles replaced.
H.229 (90); W.113 (44½); D.53 (21).

PROV: Evidently a provincial piece, almost certainly from the group of furniture made for Armley House, Leeds, which passed by descent to Mrs Frank Gott, Weetwood Garth, Leeds who bequeathed it to the City 1941.   [7.12/41]

CABINETS

33 CABINET
c.1620
Oak; various woods, possibly eucalyptus

Of rectangular gabled form with a flat lid enclosing a shallow box, the double doors open to reveal seven drawers arranged round a small central cupboard; the top pair are backed by a secret compartment and the cupboard gave access to a sideways sliding till (now missing) concealed behind the left-hand drawers; the upper stage and fitted interior have moulded beadings and all visible surfaces are richly painted in gold and silver with arabesques and pictorial panels on a black ground: the scenes portray oriental figures – as gardeners, in armed combat, fighting a dragon, with animals and seated or standing in river landscapes; the wide surrounds, drawer fronts and subsidiary panels are enhanced with a scrolling system of foliated tendrils and flowers bordered with strings; original iron hinges, locks and escutcheons, the main doors fastened by a finger latch; turned drawer knobs, the linings stained scarlet with boldly painted numbers inside; presumably originally raised on a stand or low feet.
H.66 (26); W.60 (23½); D.30 (11¾).

This cabinet belongs to a small group of furnishings apparently made in the same workshop. John Fardon owns a virtually identical model; there is a third in the V. & A. (W.9–1936) which possesses another example of more elaborate design and also a circular wooden box containing roundels decorated in the same manner, the two last items are incised 'E.W.' A closely allied ballot box dated 1619 owned by the Saddlers' Company is always accepted as giving an approximate date for the whole group which has been published as representing the kind of exotic pseudo-oriental painted furniture known at the time as 'China work' – an interesting early phase of the taste for chinoiserie (R. Edwards, 'The "Master" of the Saddlers' Ballot Box', *Burlington*, May 1936, pp.232–5). William Stokes exhibited a small oblong hanging cupboard belonging to the same family at the Harrogate Antiques Fair 1977. J. C. Irwin, *Art and the East India Trade* (V. & A. Picture Book) 1970, pl.10 illustrates a seventeenth century Indian cabinet of similar gabled form which suggests that the individual shape is inspired by oriental prototypes. The origins of this singular group of japanned furniture still poses many problems.

PROV: London Street market; bought from Charles Carey (Antiques) with the aid of a contribution from the vendor 1971.   [34/71]

34 CABINET ON STAND
Late 17th century
Walnut; pine, oak, elm

The rectangular cabinet with a moulded cornice and cushion

frieze accommodating a shallow drawer at the front is enclosed by double doors veneered in figured walnut with crossbanded borders and feathered strings; the interior is fitted with eight drawers, the divisions faced with half-round beading; mounted on a stand, containing a single long drawer, with five spiral-twist supports on bun feet connected by flat stretchers, gilt-brass escutcheons of fronded cartouche pattern, original door bolts and wired peardrop handles within; iron locks. Pine carcase with oak door panels, entirely veneered or faced in walnut; the upper stage is provided with oak drawers, the stand with an elm drawer; resurfaced top, the feet renewed in oak and three legs probably replaced.
H.130 (51½); W.76 (30); D.39 (15½).

EXH: Temple Newsam, *L.A.C.F. Members Exhibition*, 1952 (246).

PROV: Alfred Jowett; bought 1952.   [38/52]

35 CABINET
*c.*1690
Pine and oak

The rectangular cabinet is mounted on a richly carved and gilt stand with six tapered supports united by scrolled cross-stretchers and deep foliate aprons below a concave frieze; the legs, decorated with tasselled drapery and acanthus fronds, rest on twin scroll toes; the pierced cresting is ornamented with a central basket of flowers above a *lambrequin* motif, pairs of birds amid scrolling foliage and corner finials, the side crestings featuring shells; the cabinet is japanned inside and out with partly raised chinoiserie scenes in gilt on a black ground with silvered, red and brown details; the double doors enclose ten drawers of various sizes; the profiled brass corner mounts, hinges and lock plate are engraved with tight floral designs; brass ring handles. Pine stand, cresting and carcase; oak doors and drawers; the japanned surfaces are faced with veneer; the drawers are stained red inside and each backboard is painted with a black cross. The stretchers probably once supported a pair of small circular platforms for vases. Heavily regilded.
H.226 (89); W.104 (41); D.54 (21½).

There is a japanned cabinet supported by an almost identical stand, but without the cresting, at Saltram House, Devon (G. Wills, q.v., p.134, repr.).

LIT: *D.E.F.*, I, p.173, pl.24; *L.A.C.*, No.46–7 (1961), pp.12–14, repr.; G. Wills, *English Furniture 1550–1760*, 1971, p.117, repr.; F. Lewis Hinckley, *Directory of Queen Anne, Early Georgian and Chippendale Furniture*, 1971, pl.109.

PROV: By descent from Sir Thomas Colt of Puddleston Court Herefordshire to his daughter who left it to her relative K. R. Ward; purchased by the V. & A. in 1927 (No. W.46–1927); bought with the aid of a government grant 1959.   [12/59]

34

iron hinges; two engraved brass lock-plates remain.
H.244 (96).

This press was probably made by an estate joiner when the domestic offices were replanned during alterations to the west wing in 1719–20. It is positively recorded in the Temple Newsam inventory of 1808 (Y.A.S. library DD 54); 'Still-Room, Ground Floor – A large wainscot press for china with folding doors glazed and divisions, shelves and drawers in ditto 24 feet long' and presumably in an inventory of 1740 (TN EA3/21) 'Still Room – 1 Large press for China, Glasses, Sweetmeats etc.'

PROV: The Ingrams of Temple Newsam; given by the Earl of Halifax 1922.   [1922/F40]

36 PRESS FOR CHINA
*c.*1720
Oak

This china cabinet which now serves as a display case occupying three walls of a small dressing-room on the west wing was originally a fixture in the Still Room. It then had a straight front with three narrow bays (like that on the north side) but during the reconstruction in 1940 two of these were joined together to form a wider central bay and the interior was redesigned. The four pairs of double doors have fielded base panels with a rectangular pattern of glazing bars above containing the original green-tinted, streaky panes; projecting moulded cornice above a plain frieze; pegged joints;

35

36

37 CABINET ON STAND
Probably by Gillows, Lancaster
*c.*1745–50
Mahogany; oak, pine

The cabinet, of architectural design, is raised on a richly carved stand supported by cabriole legs. The central door and sides are mounted with glazed panels of chenille executed in cotton and silk against a tent stitch ground worked in black wool. The front panel depicts a basket of garden flowers on a grassy hillock, those at each end portray similar floral compositions. The cabinet is headed by a broken pediment centering on a finely carved fronded cartouche ending in a mask, the frieze is enriched with a continuous design of scrolling leaves and flower heads, while the front corners are ornamented with free-standing Corinthian columns. The side panels are surmounted by shells between paired leaves and the needlework on the front is set beneath a tinctured armorial cartouche suspending floral festoons. The interior contains twenty-two small ogee-shaped drawers arranged in two tiers flanking four graduated long drawers faced with panels of silk embroidery on a satin ground, concealing six pairs of secret drawers; the upper part is designed as a mirror-lined niche incorporating twelve Ionic columns, the floor decorated with parquetry and the ceiling with inlaid star motifs. The stand, banded with a key-pattern fret and lavishly carved with shells, rococo foliage and floral sprays is raised on massive cabriole legs connected to the apron by fronded spurs; the claw and ball feet are carved in full relief. Oak carcase veneered in mahogany with some pine inner structures.
H.206 (81); W.106 (42); D.64 (25).

37

37

The baronetcy of Bellot, Moreton, Co. Chester became extinct in 1714, but the Arms (argent, on a chief gules three cinquefoils of the field) were employed during high Victorian days by William Henry Bellot of Stockport, who displayed a romantic fondness for embellishing his possessions with them. It is virtually certain that he was responsible for carving the cartouche on this cabinet with the rather crudely-cut Bellot arms.

This cabinet is by any standards a striking piece of furniture, although at the present time it might be regarded as rather old fashioned to admire such a flamboyantly styled, even showy, piece. Two side tables with frames which relate interestingly in terms of design and enrichment to the stand are known. One of these can be provenanced to Hornblotton House, near Castle Cary, Somerset (M. Harris, *Old Furniture and Works of Decorative Art*, II, p.157); the other table was illustrated in an advertisement inserted by Biggs of Maidenhead in the *Antique Collector*, June 1955.

That this cabinet is of provincial origin is hardly in doubt; the florid carving is not of London quality, indicating the limitations of the tradesman's training and perhaps of his

tool chest. The flatness of the fronded shell enrichment on the ends is characteristic of much Irish work (the largest readily identifiable pool of provincial furniture) while the foliate cartouche is reminiscent of crestings found on furniture of the mid eighteenth century attributed to Gillows (Cave Brown Cave collection). The lack of restraint in embellishing the stand is also typical of design attitudes outside style centres not only in Dublin and Edinburgh but also the American colonies.

The way in which provincial cabinet makers exploited architectural manuals such as Batty Langley's *The Builder's Director and Bench-Mate*, 1746; various editions of the same author's *The City and Country Builder's and Workman's Treasury of Designs* and similar collections by Abraham Swann, Robert Morris and others, is only just beginning to be understood. This cabinet illustrates the manner in which such engravings served provincial workmen as a source of inspiration in the cabinet branch. The façade is conceived as a chimneypiece overmantel which, in contemporary architectural pattern books, often framed a painting. This precedent accounts for the door being fronted by a pictorial

37

panel. The Corinthian columns were doubtless copied from a drawing book; the foliate frieze, key-pattern band, broken pediment and enriched mouldings likewise have their origin in such engravings. The authors of these works were well aware of their value to provincial cabinet makers. The stand on the other hand could not be based on elements derived from pattern books published in the 1740s, in consequence it is more unorthodox and expresses greater creative flair.

The application of festive needlework panels to the front and ends is possibly unique, although at a later date some cabinets were faced with scrolled paperwork. There can be no question that they were worked for the areas they now fill and are contemporary, but the glass may have been added later. Provincial firms such as Wright and Elwick of Wakefield, advertised (c.1748) their willingness to 'draw for all Sorts of Needlework for Carpets, Beds, Firescreens, Chairs &c' and supplied ladies with 'Painted Patterns and Shades of Silk and Worsted for such works in the best manner'. That this service was in demand is shown by their Rockingham account of 1748–9 (*Furniture History*, XII (1976) p.34) – just the period of the Bellot cabinet. The interior, like the external countenance, reveals that the cabinet maker engaged his best skills while catering for the needs of a determined needlewoman. The silk panels embroidered with butterflies, caterpillars, cocks, exotic birds, bees, dragonflies and other insects amid floral sprays were evidently worked to fit their present stations. The compositions are close enough to plates in *The Ladies Amusement* 1758–60 to fuel hopes that a printed source may one day come to light.

Mrs Kathleen Taylor, one of the late Professor Bellot's executors, is quite certain that the cabinet was made by Gillows of Lancaster and remembers placing relevant evidence in one of the drawers as of interest to a would-be buyer before sending it to Sotheby's in 1969. Although the documentation has now gone astray the attribution is plausible since the Bellots were a Lancashire family – good Gillows country. The Gillow archives are patchy for the period 1740–60, but reveal that the firm made many cabinets on stands. Little of their furniture dating from the mid eighteenth century is identifiable, but Mr Cave Brown Cave's cabinet and a group represented by Cat. No.29 have been associated with Gillows and are sufficiently similar in points of detail to sustain a speculative attribution.

PROV: The Bellot family of Manchester and its environs, by descent to William Henry Bellot, surgeon, of Stockport and later Leamington, Warwickshire, grandfather of Professor Hale Bellot of High Ham, Langport, Somerset, d.1969; sold by order of his executors at Sotheby's, 3 Oct. 1969, lot 89; Nyman Bros.; Ronald A. Lee (Antiques); Hotspur Ltd; bought with the aid of a government grant 1977. [17/77]

38 COLLECTOR'S CABINET
c.1760
Mahogany; oak, pine

Of upright rectangular design in two stages separated by a narrow ledge; the upper part is enclosed by architecturally styled double doors the frieze carved with floral swags and ribbons; tapering panelled pilasters decorated with festoons headed by rococo consoles and corner blocks; dentil cornice round three sides; the lower cupboard doors are of fielded panel construction enhanced by crossbanding and corner rosettes, square bracket feet. The upper cabinet is fitted with a nest of thirty drawers in mahogany with sliding shelves above; the lower stage, also grooved for shelves, contains a deep tray which travels forwards on pairs of brass rollers; flush brass door bolts, later escutcheons. Solid mahogany sides and doors, the panelled back and internal partitions oak, pine top and baseboards.
H.173 (68); W.109 (43); D.49 (19½).

A strikingly similar cabinet in the Martin Gersh collection, New York was clearly made in the same workshop.

LIT: *Connoisseur*, Oct. 1960, p.79, repr.; *L.A.C.*, No.46–7 (1961), pp.14–18, fig.10; F. Lewis Hinckley, *Directory of Queen Anne, Early Georgian and Chippendale Furniture*, 1971, pl.97.

PROV: By descent to Miss Blanche Brooking, great-granddaughter of the 1st Earl of Harrowby; sold 1952 by Powell & Powell, Bath; W. G. Wynn Penny; Norman Adams, Ltd; bought by the L.A.C.F. 1960.
[L.A.C.F./F.12]

39 CABINET
c.1800
Satinwood and sabicu; mahogany, pine, oak, ebony, box, rosewood

In two parts divided by a ledge, the upper consists of a breakfront cabinet with three glazed doors enclosing movable shelves, the coved shoulders rise in two stages to a domed pediment incorporating a clock inscribed 'WEEKS'S / MUSEUM / TITCHBORNE STREET' and flanked by gadrooned scrolls with frond terminals; the top is accented by eight brass campana-shaped candleholders. The lower stage, which has an ormolu frieze moulding, reeded corner colonettes headed by double-leaf capitals and enriched peg feet, contains two long drawers, the upper fitted for writing and the lower for dressing with a cupboard underneath; the fall-front secretary provides a leather covered desk surface backed by six small drawers with turned ivory pulls, one being supplied with a silver-topped inkwell and sand jar; the dressing drawer is very elaborately equipped with a sliding mirror, six wells containing silver-capped cosmetic bottles, three ivory boxes, a hair brush, pincushion, six lidded compartments with slip liners, comb trays and other toilet requisites; the lids have silvered rings with bright-cut plates and the brass hardware includes die-stamped knobs and quadrant stays. The exterior is veneered with geometric panels in sabicu with satinwood surrounds, box and ebony border strings and rosewood crossbanding; lozenge-shaped panels decorate the upper sides, shelf, finial plinths and some

39

internal fitments. Mahogany carcase apart from the lower stage which has a pine back and top and an oak bottom, the main drawer bottoms and inner desk divisions are also of oak; satinwood corner colonettes; cedar slip boxes.
H.239 (94); W.101 (40); D.61 (24).

The lower cupboard formerly contained an automatic barrel-organ connected to the striking movement of the eight-day clock; this mechanism was removed about 1950, but vestiges of the apparatus remain and two plugged holes on the right side indicate where the detachable crank handle slotted. A companion cabinet owned by Lord Barnard still has the complete action which consists of two interchange-able cylinders set with pins designed as they rotate, to operate valves at the base of the organ pipes behind, a winding mechanism, a pair of bellows and various dials for selecting one of twelve tunes, regulating the speed and vol-ume. The instrument is inscribed (twice) 'Thos Weeks Tichborne Street London'. The cabinet itself is distantly related to a design dated 1791 in Thomas Sheraton's *Drawing-*

Book, pl.48.

Seventeen other cabinets of closely similar design have been recorded, many retain the original clock and silver fitments, bearing date letters registered between 1798 and 1808; a large number of virtually identical cabinets were therefore made over at least a decade. It is obvious that they were connected with the renowned museum of 'mechanical curiosities' which Thomas Weeks established at Nos.3 & 4 Titchborne Street about 1797. The premises included a large exhibition gallery with an adjoining shop, suggesting that provision was made for the public to order examples of certain models displayed in the gallery. Joseph Beloudy supplied a number of 'self-acting organs' to the museum and the cabinets would presumably be made by a London firm. Unfortunately, none of the so-called Weeks' cabinets or other pieces displaying convincing stylistic affinities with the main group, bear a maker's label and no documentary evi-dence for their authorship has come to light. Particulars of twenty-three members of this 'family' were published in the *Connoisseur*, May 1971, pp.13–21 and details of a further seven

39

(Lord Barnard)

examples are preserved in the files at Temple Newsam. Another factor supporting the view that the cabinets were commissioned by Weeks is their striking resemblance to the façade of his museum, a tall, narrow building surmounted by a pediment rising – like the shoulders of the cabinets – in two curved stages to a gadrooned cresting featuring a clock.

LIT: E. T. Joy, 'A Cabinet from Weeks' Museum', *Connoisseur*, June 1965, pp.117–19, pl.4 (colour); *L.A.C.*, No.58 (1966), p.3, repr.; *Burlington*, July 1966, p.373, fig.54; C. G. Gilbert, 'Some Weeks' Cabinets Reconsidered', *Connoisseur*, May 1971, pp.13–21, repr. (colour); L. G. Langwill and N. Boston, *Church and Chamber Barrel Organs* (2nd ed.), 1970, p.66.

PROV: Leonard Knight Ltd; private collection; Sotheby's, 10 Dec. 1964, lot 290; Pelham Galleries; Hotspur Ltd; bought with the aid of a government grant 1965.   [10/65]

40 MUSIC CABINET
By Marsh and Jones, Leeds probably to the design of Charles Bevan
*c.*1866
Satinwood; rosewood, mahogany, maple, ebony, etc.

In the form of a two-tier stand, the lower stage enclosed by double-doors with an open shelf raised on column supports above. The doors are of framed panel construction, faced with marquetry roundels in various coloured woods on a brown-stained bird's-eye maple ground; the ends and back are of simulated tongue and grooved plank construction. The square chamfered corner-posts united by shaped and inlaid cross rails, are continued above the middle shelf as turned lotus columns, the shafts headed by elaborate inlaid blocks with pierced spandrels capped by lotus-bud finials. Brass bolt and pin-hinges, white pottery castors. Constructed of satinwood with rosewood columns, the shelves are veneered on to mahogany boards. A slot in the back was cut when a radiogram was installed.
H.94 (37); W.64 (25); D.39 (15½).

The underside of the top shelf bears a label inscribed 'MARSH AND JONES / (Late KENDELL & CO) / No. 17459 / Workman's Name. Benjⁿ Smith.'

The cabinet is similar in many respects to Charles Bevan's design for a music canterbury executed by Marsh and Jones for Titus Salt in 1866 – reproduced *Building News*, 1 March 1867. The inlaid decoration and detailing is also closely related to Bevan's design for a davenport made by Marsh and Jones and displayed in their showrooms in Margaret Street, Cavendish Square, London – illustrated *Building News*, 1865, pp.183 and 191. These stylistic analogies suggest that Charles Bevan designed this music cabinet.

LIT: L. O. J. Boynton, 'High Victorian Furniture: The Example of Marsh and Jones of Leeds', *Furniture History*, III (1967), pp.54–91, esp. pl.20; C. Hutchinson, 'Furniture by Marsh and Jones of Leeds 1864–1872', *L.A.C.*, No.80 (1977), p.15, fig.4.

EXH: Temple Newsam, *Furniture Made in Yorkshire 1750–1900*, 1974 (19).

PROV: Reeves Ltd (Auctioneers), Croydon (*c.*1960); Mrs Davidson How; bought 1976.   [34/76]

40

41 CORNER CABINET
By Ernest Gimson (Daneway Workshop, Gloucestershire)
1903
Oak; holly, ebony

The upper stage is of concave polygonal plan glazed with rectangular panes and enclosed by two doors set between a central pier and tower corners, the subsidiary glazing bars are decorated with inlaid chequered bands of holly and ebony; simply moulded base and cornice, the interior stained black, fitted with four shelves. The lower cupboard, containing a narrow shelf, is enclosed by splayed doors of raised panel construction mounted on pin-hinges and headed by a bow-fronted ledge, the side staves are continued down to form straight legs; panelled back, revealed tenon joints. Original faceted pear-drop handles in bronze on the upper doors made by Alfred Bucknell, a matching pair on the lower cupboard replaced at an early date by another set conforming to one of Bucknell's patterns. Locks impressed 'CHUBB & CO / LONDON / MACHINE MADE'.
H.213 (84); W.112 (44); D.76 (30).

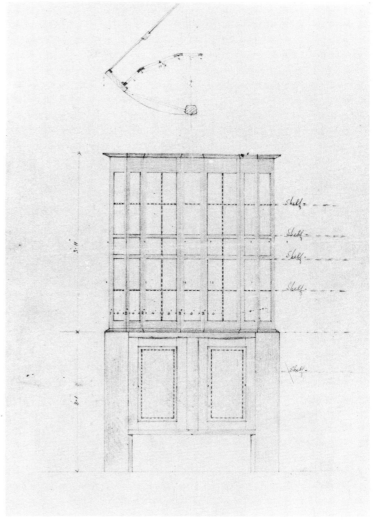

41

41

The drawing for this china cabinet or more accurately, 'corner dresser', is preserved amongst the Gimson designs at Cheltenham Art Gallery (MN.P.1941/222/245), pencil and brown crayon, 14 × 19 in. The piece was illustrated in the *Art Journal* in 1904 captioned 'Designed by Ernest W. Gimson. Made by P. Waals'. Peter Van Der Waals was Gimson's foreman at the Daneway Workshop, near Sapperton, Gloucestershire and Alfred Bucknell forged hardware for the furniture.

LIT: J. A. Gotch, 'Modern Furniture', *Art Journal*, May 1904, p.137, repr.; *L.A.C.*, No.63 (1968), p.4, repr.; *Burlington*, June 1970, p.396, fig.69; G. Wills, *English Furniture 1760–1900*, 1971, p.248, pl.198.

EXH: London, *8th Arts and Crafts Exhibition*, 1906 (264), price £28.10.0; Leicester, *Ernest Gimson*, 1969 (LR.9).

PROV: Bought from Gimson by Harry H. Peach, Dryad Works, Leicester in 1915 (one of many pieces by Gimson acquired for his private home Crowbank, Leicester); by descent to Roger Peach whose widow sold the cabinet at Christie's, 18 July 1968, lot 334; bought through H. Blairman & Sons 1968. [23.1/68]

42 CHINA CABINET (VITRINE)

By Gillow & Co., Lancaster
1907
Kingwood, walnut, oak

In the form of an upright serpentine-fronted cabinet glazed with curvilinear panes; the two adjustable tray shelves are enclosed by a door in the central section which rises to a coved platform top flanked by lower side-ledges for displaying a set of three vases; the shaped base is raised on four keeled cabriole legs furnished with ormolu toe and knee mounts; the framework is outlined with gilt-bronze mouldings, richly fronded border-scrolls and elaborate shoulder ornaments in the rococo style. Oak carcase veneered with kingwood, walnut shelves and beading, the back of framed panel construction; pin-hinges; decorated ormolu key.
H.178 (70); W.132 (52); D.35 (14).

A vitrine of corresponding design is illustrated in a trade catalogue titled *Examples of Furniture and Decoration by Gillows*, n.d. [*c*.1905–10]. p.105 with the caption 'P.6429 A very

graceful Louis XV VITRINE, made of kingwood with Bronze Mounts, Mercury Gilt, most carefully finished in all details.' Originally backed by mirror plates.

PROV: Bought by Sam Wilson from Gillow & Co. for the drawing room at Rutland Lodge, Leeds in July 1907 and entered in his notebook as '1 Louis XV vitrine with ormolu mounts £185'; the Sam Wilson Bequest 1925. [S.W.222]

CELLARETS

43 CELLARET

c.1785
Mahogany; pine

Octagonal with slightly tapered sides, a flat hinged top and four straight splayed legs of square section, the lid is outlined with a corner moulding and the base has a plain band; the interior is divided with radial partitions for nine bottles; original brass side handles and castors, the front swing handle replaced by a lock plate, lead lining removed. Solid mahogany with a pine base, divisions and rails.
H.72 (28½); Diam. 57 (22½).

PROV: Recorded in the 1930s Lotherton inventory; the Gascoigne gift 1968. [7.166/68]

44 CELLARET

c.1805
Mahogany; rosewood, beech, pine, oak

Of oblong sarcophagus form supported by four recumbent sphinx resting on a low platform with concealed castors; the sloping lid and sides inlaid with brass strings and cross-banded in rosewood, the base ornamented with a reeded strip between brass beading, the platform also finished with brass corner beads; the carved Egyptian sphinx are painted to simulate bronze; ormolu lion's-mask drop-ring handles; lead-lined interior partitioned for ten bottles; the lock impressed 'I. BRAMAH PATENT' with a Royal crown. The pine undercarriage and mahogany chest faced with mahogany veneer; internal divisions and bottom board oak, copper plate screwed inside apex of lid to prevent springing.
H.49 (19½); W.92 (36½); D.57 (22¼).

Sheraton observed that cellarets were, as a rule 'large enough to hold . . . ten round wine bottles' and writing of open wine-coolers in 1803 he commented they 'are not so generally used as they were, and amongst the higher classes are wholly laid aside' having been superseded by models 'in the figure of ancient stone coffins'. In 1808 George Smith recommended the use of mahogany for cellarets of sarcophagus form 'the ornaments of which may be carved and bronzed' and noted 'they should be lined with lead' and

44

'have castors concealed in the plinth'. This example is clearly highly typical of the period.

LIT: *L.A.C.*, No.52 (1963), p.6, fig.2; C. G. Gilbert, *L.G. & R. F.*, 1972, p.43, repr.

PROV: Agnes and Norman Lupton Bequest 1953.

[13.382/53]

SUITES

Seat Furniture

45 SUITE OF TWENTY CHAIRS, FOUR SETTEES AND A DAY-BED

By James Pascall, London
1746
Gilt beech; walnut

The entire suite is covered with wool needlework executed in tent-stitch, stuffed over the rails and fastened down by round-headed brass nails cast in one piece; the many-coloured design of garden flowers, all depicted larger than life and shaded to give the appearance of relief, is worked in the opposite direction to the greenish-gold ground, some flower centres are enhanced with French knots and the double-headed day-bed has two roll bolsters. The settees are raised on six- and the bed on eight-hipped cabriole legs bordered by C-scrolls and ornamented with a hatched flame cartouche; the leafy pad feet conceal castors with leather rollers; the settees have curved flattened arms enriched with flame-work and fronds terminating in shaggy monster heads, the supports are carved with beaded acanthus and scrolls. Beech frames with walnut arms on the settees, dipped underbraces on the settee and day-bed, original webbing, canvas and hair stuffing, local restorations.
Chairs: H.92 (36½); W.67 (26½); D.59 (23).

45

Settees: H.104 (41); W.170 (67); D.79 (31).
Day-bed: H.86 (34); L.216 (85); W.86 (34).

This set formed part of a larger suite commissioned by Henry 7th Viscount Irwin of Temple Newsam for the Long Gallery which he completely redesigned between 1738 and 1745 (C. G. Gilbert, *Connoisseur*, q.v.). It comprised, in addition, a pair of console tables Cat. No.450, a pair of side tables and eight torchères Cat. No.353 which almost certainly relate to a payment dated 7 Aug. 1746 to 'James Pascall, London, 4 Tables, 2 Settees, etc. £364.16.0'. Very little is known about his activites other than scattered references in Sir Richard Hoare's Private Accounts recording various payments to 'Mr Pascall the carver and gilder' or 'framemaker' and his wife Ann between 1733 and 1751. A pair of matching stools made in the nineteenth century are now at Garrowby, Yorkshire.

In March 1745 Sir Edward Gascoigne wrote to Lord Irwin from Cambray in France 'I think ye Tapestry-work Chairs here do look very well, & even not unworthy a place in ye handsommest Apartment in England, such as I think yt you are furnishing'. He went on to compare the cost of seat covers worked in England and Cambray, pointing out that London prices were double and recommended that 'It might be worth my Ladys while to have a handsome design

45

45

work, a large double headed couch with carved and gilt legs and stuffed and covered with fine needlework and 2 Bolsters', all were equipped with 'Green and white check cases'; by descent to the Earl of Halifax; given by Sir Henry Price, Sir Montague Burton, Mr Charles Brotherton and Mr Frank Parkinson with the aid of a contribution from the N.A.C.F. 1939. [16.1–25/39]

46 SET OF FOUR ARMCHAIRS AND A SOFA
By William Fell and Lawrence Turton, London
1771
Beech

The gilt chairs are designed with oval, slightly-curved backs supported on acanthus stays, swept arms and square tapered legs enriched with overlapping coin rosettes; the padded arm rests carved with husks, are united to the back frames by leafy scrolls while the serpentine-fronted seat rails are ornamented with fluting between pearl-beaded and twisted ribbon mouldings. The legs, headed by patera blocks end in turned leaf-cup feet. The sofa is basically of identical design except for the absence of an open gap between seat and back and the existence of eight legs; the original cross-braces have been replaced by three iron tie-rods, the back is reinforced behind with two struts. The Gobelins tapestry covers are woven in wool with a high proportion of silk on a *damas cramoisy* ground; the backs display colourful bunches of garden flowers tied with ribbons, the seats are strewn with floral sprays and the arm pads portray various blossoms; the panels are all different. Modern webbing and pleated backing material.
Chairs: H.97 (38½); W.71 (28); D.64 (25).
Sofa: H.109 (43); W.211 (83); D.74 (29).

These pieces are from a suite commissioned by Sir Lawrence Dundas for his tapestry drawing room at Moor Park, Hertfordshire. In 1784 the wall tapestries and furnishings were installed by his son at 19 Arlington Street, London and remained together until 1934 when the majority of the wall hangings were taken to Aske Hall, Yorkshire, where they remain; the other tapestry furnishings were sold. One sofa, six armchairs, two window stools and two firescreens passed to the Philadelphia Museum of Art (1941. 6. 1–11), the four remaining armchairs and a sofa with two cushions are now at Temple Newsam House.

Fell and Turtons' account for this suite (preserved in the North Yorkshire Record Office ZNK X 1/7/11) is dated 1771, but records only two sofas, six chairs and two window stools, the companion pieces must therefore have been supplied slightly later. The invoice includes

To 2 Sophas Carved and gilt in Burnished gold, stuffed with Best Curl'd hair and fine linnin . . . £25	50	0	0
To Covering do with your Tapestry, used Brass nails sewing silk, fine Durant for the back Backs, tax &c	1	10	0
To 6 Elbow Chairs carv'd and gilt in Burnished gold stuffd in Best Curl'd hair and fine linnin . . . £10	60	0	0

45

or two drawn & sent over, yr so she might have something quite new . . . and ye better ye painting ye better would his work be' (TN CORR 16/44A). Evidently Lord Irwin chose to upholster the suite in more durable wool needlework of English origin. However, Lord Halifax owns a floral-tapestry firescreen formerly at Temple Newsam embroidered 'FAIT. A. CAMBRAY. PAR. I. BAERT. LE. 15. FEVRIER. 1744' – evidently a gift from Sir Edward to illustrate the tapestry weavers' skill. See C. G. Gilbert, 'A Present from Cambray', *L.A.C.*, No.77 (1975) p.24.

LIT: F. Lenygon, *Furniture in England 1660–1760*, 1914, pls. 78, 118, 141, 143; *Apollo*, July 1938, p.16, figs. v & vi; *Apollo*, Dec. 1941, pp.137–8, fig.1; *Furniture History*, III (1967), pp.26–7; C. G. Gilbert, 'The Temple Newsam Suite of early Georgian gilt Furniture', *Connoisseur*, Feb. 1968, pp.84–88.

EXH: Temple Newsam, *Pictures and Furniture*, 1938 (198–222); *Temple Newsam Heirlooms*, 1972 (26).

PROV: Made for Henry 7th Viscount Irwin and recorded in the 1808 inventory of Temple Newsam '10th Room Picture Gallery First Floor – 20 large backstools the legs carved and gilt and stuffed and covered with fine flowered needlework, 4 large settees with carved and gilt arms and legs and stuffed and covered with fine flowered needle-

To Covering do with your Tapestry used
sewing silk fine Durant for the Back

Backs tax &c	2	8	0
paper Cases for the sophas stools & Chairs		15	0
packing the 2 Sophas in 2 Cases used screws			
Nails paper &c	2	3	0
packing the 6 Chairs in Three Cases used			
screws nails paper &c	2	18	0
going down self and man to unpack Do		12	0
Expences going and Comming Back		3	6

Little is known about Lawrence Fell, except that he formed a partnership with William Turton in 1770, was employed at Burghley House and, according to Sir Lawrence Dundas's bank account, received over £5,000 between 1765 and 1775 for work at Moor Park and 19 Arlington Street, which included equipping the magnificent tapestry drawing room. The seven surviving bills thus document only a fraction of this commission.

Thirteen sets of medallion tapestry hangings were woven on the Gobelins looms between 1764 and 1789 of which six went to English customers, all of whom ordered both wall hangings and furniture covers. Sir Lawrence Dundas was one of the few patrons to commission a set woven on a grey *damas cramoisy* ground and his tapestry room at Moor Park is more impressively documented than any other. Four letters from Jacques Neilson, *entrepreneur* of the *basse lisse*, to Thomas Dundas who handled the transaction for his brother, survive: the earliest, dated 19 January 1767, refers to the tapestries as already underway, while the last, written on 3 July 1769 concerns arrangements for delivery. Neilson's bill of 1769 only mentions wall panels and covers for six chairs, two sofas, two window seats and a firescreen. The covers for the other four chairs and additional firescreens were probably ordered in 1771 since Thomas Dundas's bank account shows further payments to Neilson between 1772 and 1775 which must relate to these purchases.

The following is an excerpt from Neilson's invoice, on the half leaf of a letter dated 15 May 1769.

Plus six fauteuiles de Parade a 300 chacun	1800
Plus deux canapes evalue pour huis fauteuils	2400
Plus un nouvel Ecran	240

Suites of designs for furniture covers were produced at the Gobelins between 1760 and 1767 by Maurice Jacques and Louis Tessier '*peintre de fleurs au Gobelins*'. The majority of cartoons were contributed by Tessier and a score or so of his floral compositions for backs, seats and arm pads survive at the Musée des Gobelins, Paris, including all the original coloured cartoons for the chair seats (248/11–16–19–22) and

46

46

46

46

two back panels (248/26–29) on the Moor Park chairs now at Temple Newsam. The panels were woven to a standard cartouche-shaped size which would fit any normal chair frames and most of the patterns are matched on the floral-tapestry suites supplied to the Earl of Coventry at Croome Court (now in the Metropolitan Museum of Art, New York) and William Weddell of Newby Hall, Yorkshire.

The commissioning of these celebrated tapestries is the subject of an important article by Eileen Harris, 'The Moor Park Tapestries', *Apollo*, Sept. 1967, pp.180–9; Jacques Neilson's letters and accounts (North Yorkshire Record Office, ZNK X 1/7/50–55) were reprinted in Christie's *Arlington Street Sale Catalogue*, 26 April 1934, pp.43–6; Maurice Fenaille's *Etat Général des Tapisseries de la Manufacture des Gobelins*, Vol.IV, 1907, contains many illustrations and much useful background information, while an excellent account of the related tapestry room from Croome Court by James Parker and Edith Standen is to be found in *Decorative Art from the Kress Collection*, 1964, pp.3–57. The majority of illustrations supporting previous discussions of the Moor Park suite reproduce examples acquired by the Philadelphia Museum of Art.

LIT (only the principle references are cited): *Country Life*, 24 Sept. 1921, pp.350–5, figs.2, 4, 5; A. T. Bolton, *The Architecture of Robert and James Adam*, II, 1922, pp.295–9; F. Kimball, 'The Moor Park Tapestry Suite', *Apollo*, July 1941, pp.23–5; E. Harris, 'Robert Adam and the Gobelins', *Apollo*, April 1962, pp.100–6; E. Harris, 'The Moor Park Tapestries', *Apollo*, Sept. 1967, pp.180–9.

PROV: Sir Lawrence Dundas, Moor Park, Hertfordshire; removed by his son to 19 Arlington Street, London, in 1784 and thence by descent to the Marquess of Zetland; Christie's, 26 April 1934, lot 81; Lancelot Hugh Smith; the Hon. H. A. Vivian Smith; Christie's, 22 Oct. 1953, lot 89; Alfred Pearson; Sotheby's, 26 May 1967, lot 178; ? Holborn; purchased from the executors of Sir David Ross (d.1971) with the aid of a government grant and contributions from the L.A.C.F., N.A.C.F. and a private benefactor 1975.   [66/75]

CHAIRS

Backstools, Child's, Curricle, Garden, Hall, Master's, Revolving, etc.

47 ARMCHAIR
*c.*1600
Cedar; oak

The open arcaded back, divided by vase-shaped uprights, is richly carved with interlace designs, stylized foliage, gadroons and linear patterns; the heraldic cresting consists of unicorn supporters gorged with chains, wearing *fleurs-de-lys* on the shoulder and backed by pennants incised C and A; the shield

bears a lion-rampant surmounted by a Tudor rose and flanked by Greek lambda and alpha signs; the curved sloping arms, embellished with ferns, rest on bulbous frond-carved supports; deep seat-rails styled with a rope moulding between rows of nail-heads and a gouged border enriched with stamps; turned bulbous front legs with herring-bone patterns; the lower cross-rail, stretchers and base of each leg have been renewed in oak; the back-post and apex finials, unicorns' horns and ears missing; nailed oak seat, pegged construction.
H.130 (51½); W.74 (29); D.49 (19½).

The armorials are of an hereditary Keepership or Wardenship and obviously relate to the owners of Hornby Castle, built by Sir William Conyers (d.1524) whose mother was daughter of the last Lord Fauconberg; they also feature in an heraldic display over a late medieval doorway formerly at Hornby. The unicorns, Greek and Lombardic letters are obscure, but it may be significant that in the time of Edward I the Fauconberg lion was 'differenced on the shoulder with a *fleurs-de-lys*' and the initials might stand for Lady Anne Conyers.

Three other armchairs with open arcaded backs, heraldic crestings and enriched frames of very similar design are known, each is of oak and has a north country provenance. The first example, stated to come from Wordsworth's house, Ambleside, Westmorland, was illustrated in *Connoisseur*, April 1920, p.xxx and after heavy restoration purchased by Sir William Burrell; it is now in the collection of Glasgow Art Gallery and Museum. The second model which offers a very close analogy to the Hornby Castle chair was bought in Otley, Yorkshire and later acquired by T. G. Burns of Rous Lench Court (*Antique Collector*, 1958, p.220, repr.). The third specimen, at Norton Conyers, Yorkshire, dated 1603, is illustrated by C. Latham, *In English Homes*, I, 1904, p.ix. Although all four chairs have in varying degrees been restored they express a strong regional character indigenous to the north-western border counties.

LIT (only important references are cited): P. Macquoid, *The Age of Oak*, 1904, p.55, pl.lv (colour); *Country Life*, 14 July 1906, p.64, repr.; *D.E.F.*, I, p.228 and fig.10; *Antique Collector*, June 1967, p.118, repr.

EXH: London, V. & A., *International Art Treasures*, 1962 (63); Temple Newsam, *Oak Furniture from Lancashire and the Lake District*, 1973 (13).

PROV: Hornby Castle, Yorkshire which descended through the families of Conyers and Darcy to that of Osborne, Dukes of Leeds; a tablet on the underside inscribed 'HORNBY CASTLE / COLLECTION / APRIL 1930' shows it was withheld from the Hornby sale in June 1930, another label printed 'LADY GLAMIS' indicates it passed to the third daughter of the 10th Duke of Leeds before reverting to the 11th Duke who sold it at Sotheby's, 14 July 1961, lot 140; S. W. Wolsey (Antiques); bought with the aid of a government grant 1962.
                          [12.2/62]

47

48 ARMCHAIR
17th century, third quarter
Oak

Of rectangular design, the front uprights formed as Tuscan columns with 'vase and cover' arm supports and pegged block joints; the legs are connected by low grooved stretchers; square back posts, slightly dipped arms ending in scrolls, the stuffed seat and padded back are covered in calf leather secured by brass nails. The frame is extensively repaired; restorations include blocks under the rear legs, replacement of two stretchers, arm-shafts with married scroll terminals and insertion of a new under back rail two inches above the original. The front corner blocks, arms and back support were formerly sheathed in leather.
H.106 (42); W.60 (23½); D.41 (16¼).

PROV: Purchased from Phillips of Hitchin by Guy Ferrand, Morland Hall, Hants, *c.*1920; bought from his son H. W. J. Ferrand 1954   [11.1/54]

48

49 ARMCHAIR
17th century, second half
Oak

Of rectangular design, the spirally turned and blocked front uprights connected to the back posts by double stretcher rails with a single high spiral stretcher in front; the calf leather seat and back panels are packed with straw and secured by brass nails; slightly dipped arms originally sheathed in leather; pegged construction. This chair is heavily restored; the evidence of reconstruction plainly indicates that the frame has been rebuilt with the insertion of new timber and the front members are unlikely to have formed part of the original structure.
H.101 (40); W.61 (24); D.44 (17½).

Pauline Agius published a somewhat similar set of chairs made locally for Christ Church, Oxford, in 1692, *Furniture History*, VII (1971), pl.24B.

PROV: Purchased from Phillips of Hitchin by Guy Ferrand, Morland Hall, Hants, *c*.1920; bought from his son H.W.J. Ferrand 1954.   [11.2/54]

49

50

50 ARMCHAIR
c.1670
Oak

The back is constructed of wide uprights and rails framing a sunk panel bordered by chip-carved mouldings, the side staves are decorated with pairs of tulips and daisies and the lower crossbar with heart-shaped fronds; the top rail is fashioned as an open-arched cresting centering on a tablet enriched with an inverted botanical motif; long scrolled and ridged ear pieces, the panel carved with a Tudor rose and tulip design; plank seat, baluster turned and blocked uprights supporting dipped arms; the front rail is ornamented with a running tulip pattern, moulded side rails, low stretchers on three sides; of nailed and pegged construction, some joints reinforced with iron straps. The legs are slightly cut down and the rear stretcher is missing.
H.115 (45½); W.65 (25½); D.43 (17)

The curious stepped and spired foliate motif on the cresting tablet is difficult to interpret; it might be an inverted stylized tulip or possibly a religious emblem related to incised patterns on grave slabs where the hill of Calvary is traditionally represented as a stepped mount. Nail holes in the back suggest the cresting at one time supported a finial – possibly a cross. An armchair of closely similar design was advertised in *Country Life*, 23 June 1976, p.70; there is another of comparable pattern in the Burrell Collection, Glasgow.

LIT: *Country Life*, 14 July 1906, p.64, repr.

PROV: Formerly at Hornby Castle, Yorkshire and possibly recorded in an inventory of 1839 (Y.A.S. DD5 Box 20/5) 'Tower Room – A Carved oak armchair', a tablet on the underside inscribed 'HORNBY CASTLE / COLLECTION / APRIL 1930' indicates it was withheld from the Hornby Castle sale in June 1930; by descent to the 11th Duke of Leeds; Sotheby's, 14 July 1961, lot 141; S. W. Wolsey (Antiques); bought with the aid of a government grant 1962. [12.3/62]

51 ARMCHAIR
17th century, last quarter
Oak

The back panel is carved in flat relief with a formal pattern of stylized tulips and foliate crosses within a linear system of

51

circles and lozenges on a stippled ground, headed by a scrolled pediment enriched with fronds and gouge-cut bands; the sloping arms rest on double baluster supports decorated with groove- and ring-turning and a knop above the stretchers; channelled rails and back posts, scalloped seat board, pegged construction.
H.114 (45); W.64 (25); D.43 (17).

The cresting is reinforced behind with iron ties; over-large mortice slots and packing of the upper joints suggest the arms are not original.

PROV: Edmund Leatham, Wentbridge House, Yorkshire; inherited by Lady Gascoigne; the Gascoigne gift 1968. [7.146/68]

52 SET OF ONE ARM AND TWO SINGLE CHAIRS
Late 17th century
Oak

Of framed panel back design, the flattened crestings pierced with paired scrolls and frets; the panels, contained in moulded borders, are carved with formalized carnations, tulips, grapes and daisies amid a system of scrolling tendrils; the rails and crestings are decorated with sunk patterns stained

52

black; square posts with pyramidal caps, the front uprights turned as Tuscan columns; plank seats, sloped arms, plain stretchers, pegged construction. The armchair is branded 'FH' and one single bears the initials 'IC', both marks struck on the backs.
Armchair: H.106 (42); W.61 (24); D.43 (17).
Single: H.96 (38); W.46 (18); D.39 (15½).

These chairs are heavily restored: the stretchers, rails and seats are all renewed, the feet of one single chair have been replaced and the other has a new cresting; the rebuilding was almost certainly undertaken by a dealer who attempted to achieve a uniform surface tone by a liberal use of stain and varnish.

Many chairs of closely similar design are known, striking analogies are illustrated by R. Edwards, *English Chairs*, H.M.S.O., 1970, fig.16; H. Cescinsky, *Early English Furniture and Woodwork*, 1927, Vol.I, p.200, fig.268 and there is another example in Leathley church, Yorkshire (*Oak Furniture from Yorkshire Churches*, T.N. Exhib. Cat. 1971, (23) repr.). The type is common in Cheshire. An armchair of identical pattern, also stamped 'FH' on the back panel was exhibited by W. Stokes (Antiques) at the Harrogate Antique Dealers' Fair in 1974.

LIT: *Antique Collector*, Sept/Oct. 1944, repr. (set of three); G. Wills, *English Furniture 1550–1760*, 1971, p.68, pl.55; C. G. Gilbert, 'Regional Traditions in English Vernacular Furniture', *Winterthur Conference Report*, 1974, pp.43–77, fig.2.

PROV: Leonard Knight, Ltd; bought 1944. [29.1–3/44]

53 ARMCHAIR
Possibly by Richard Price, London
c.1680
Walnut

Of rectangular design with caned back and seat panels; the spirally-turned members are sectioned by blocks carved with daisies; the back posts are surmounted by crown finials and the front uprights terminate in furred lion's-paw feet; slightly dipped moulded arms with fronded volutes; the seat rails are enriched with acanthus and the back panel is set within an openwork frame of scrolling foliage and roses surmounted by a pierced cresting ornamented with *amorini* supporting a crown amid oak leaves; the high front stretcher centres on a crown flanked by foliage; pegged construction; legs slightly cut down.
H.115 (45½); W.61 (24); D.43 (17).

The frame is stamped 'R P' on the inside edge of the back panel (three times), under each arm and behind the left splat. A child's high-chair of very similar design illustrated in Sir A. Heal's *London Furniture Makers 1660–1840*, fig.52 also

bears this mark and it has been suggested by R. W. Symonds that the initials stand for Richard Price, joiner, who is known to have made caned 'Elbowe chaires of the twisted turne of Wallnut wood with wrought mouldings, rails and Lyons feet' for the Royal palaces between *c*.1676–83 (*Connoisseur*, Feb. 1934, pp.86–92). The Royal crown is certainly a conspicuous feature of this chair which, in elaboration and quality, is consistent with what one might expect a leading chairmaker to produce.

RP

LIT: *Burlington*, June 1970, p.399 & fig.72; *Collector's Guide*, Jan. 1971, p.67, repr.; G. Wills, *English Furniture 1550–1760*, 1971, p.84, pl.67.

PROV: Maxwell Joseph; Sotheby's, 19 Dec. 1969, lot 77; Stair & Co; H. Blairman & Sons; bought 1969. [30/69]

53

54 PAIR OF CHAIRS
Possibly by Richard Bealing, London
*c.*1685
Walnut

Of upright rectangular design with caned panels; the elaborately turned back posts are capped by dome finials and sectioned by blocked joints ornamented with daisies; the oval back and circular seat panels are framed by flattened scrolls and the cresting and front stretcher are richly carved with a pierced composition of *amorini* supporting a crown, the upper pair blowing trumpets; the front legs of moulded scroll form are connected to the rear legs by turned side stretchers with medial and high back bars; the surface is textured with stippling and stamps; pegged construction. The crestings are backed by a finger-grip block, one is braced with iron straps and inscribed '18/11/46'.
H.117 (40); W.49 (19½); D.40 (16).

One chair is impressed 'R.B.' (twice) inside the rim of the caned back; the initials may relate to Richard Bealing who supplied walnut seat furniture to William III. A Chair of closely similar design and character is illustrated by H. E. Binstead, *English Chairs*, 1923, pl.v.

LIT: G. Wills, *English Furniture 1550–1760*, 1971, p.85, pl.68.

PROV: S. W. Wolsey (Antiques); bought with the aid of a government grant 1962.   [12.4/62]

55 BACKSTOOL
*c.*1700
Oak

The back, which frames an oblong panel, has a broad crest rail carved with a leaf meander and the arcaded lower rail is decorated with turned pendants; the ornamental split-balusters applied to the back panel and posts, the pierced ears and pendants are not original, seat renewed. The block-turned front legs are united by a spiral-twist bar and the side stretchers are bridged by a baluster-turned crossmember; front feet renewed. The top rail has a channelled finger grip.
H.101 (40); W.46 (18); D.38 (15).

The carved cresting is similar to the top rail on a chest in Lancaster priory church. An interesting north country backstool with some antiquarian improvements.

PROV: Given by William Stokes, Cold Overton Hall, Rutland 1976   [33/76]

56 CHAIR
*c.*1725
Walnut; beech

The bold, vase-shaped, splat is connected by spurs to hooped uprights which centre on a scroll cresting carved with a fronded-shell motif; the curvilinear slip seat is raised on hipped cabriole forelegs ornamented with shells and husk pendants, terminating in claw and ball feet; spatular rear feet. Walnut with beech rails and seat base, the moulded shoe, splat, uprights and seat rails are veneered with figured walnut; united by screws and pegs; upholstered in modern damask; incised (twice) 'III'.
H.102 (40½); W.56 (22); D.49 (19¼).

LIT: *Apollo*, Dec. 1941, p.140, fig.6.

PROV: H. Blairman & Sons; bought 1941.   [22/41]

55   56

57 CHAIR

*c.*1720–30
Walnut; beech, oak

The upright rectangular back and splayed seat are raised on hipped cabriole legs ending in formalised hoof feet with brass rims; the legs and seat rails are veneered in burr walnut enriched with gilt gesso borders, frond-carved knees and brackets while the front seat rail centres on a fanned husk pendant; the gilt details are textured with cross-hatching and circular stamps; upholstered in contemporary bottle-green silk velvet laid on to unbleached calico stuffed over the rails and held by brass nails; the back is webbed and backed by a later linen secured with gold silk piping; fragments of a red material may indicate the original backing; curled hair stuffing.
H.105 (41½); W.59 (23); D.56 (22).

This chair is from a set of six sold at Sotheby's in 1960, one was acquired by the V. & A. (W.15–1960); a pair went to the Metropolitan Museum of Art and another pair to Melbourne Art Gallery, Australia. The frames and upholstery of this set are identical to a very large suite comprising settees, winged easy chairs, stools and side chairs at Houghton Hall, Norfolk, although there is no proof that they come from this collection. The Houghton chairs have a silver galloon trimming instead of nails.

LIT: The chairs of identical pattern at Houghton Hall have frequently been discussed, illustrated and exhibited. Only publications which reproduce the example at Temple Newsam are cited: *L.A.C.*, No.46–7 (1961) pp.12–14, figs.7 & 8.

PROV: Perhaps from Houghton Hall, Norfolk (Sir Robert Walpole) and by descent to the Marquess of Cholmondeley; G. Jetley (Antiques); Sotheby's, 29 Jan. 1960, lot 117; Phillips of Hitchin; bought with the aid of a government grant 1960.   [16/60]

58 MASTER'S CHAIR

*c.*1730
Walnut; elm, beech, pine, sycamore

Of curvilinear design with a high back, concave vase-shaped splat and broad sloping shoulders ornamented with carved and gilt acanthus, volute terminals and a scroll cresting surmounted by an eagle displayed; the upper splat is inlaid with a wreath suspended from ribbon ties and the backposts with husk pendants; lion's-head arm terminals; rounded slip seat covered in hide; cabriole forelegs on pad feet. Veneered in richly figured walnut with decorative inlay of dyed and natural sycamore, solid walnut forelegs and arms, stained elm back posts and splat, beech seat frame, gilt pine cresting with traces of green paint; the frame united by pegs.
H.208 (82); W. at shoulders 104 (41); D.53 (21).

A Master's chair of identical design and proportions but with a slightly different pattern of inlaid husk pendants and a panel of floral marquetry instead of a wreath was acquired from a local source by Aldric Young (Antiques) Edinburgh in 1974. This example is inlaid across the top 'FOR OUR COUNTRY' but the carved and gilt eagle and acanthus cresting was a Victorian copy of the original and has been scrapped. Both chairs are clearly from the same workshop.

LIT: *Burlington*, Nov. 1918, pp.163–4, repr.; R. W. Symonds, *The Present State of Old English Furniture*, 1921, fig.1; H. A. Tipping, *English Furniture of the Cabriole Period*, 1927, pl.x; R. W. Symonds, *English Furniture from Charles I to George II*, 1929, pp.38–9, figs.16 & 18; *Antique Collector*, Nov./Dec. 1944, p.202, repr.; *Connoisseur*, Dec. 1959, p.267, repr.

PROV: Percival Griffiths; Christie's, 11 May 1939, lot 184; R. W. Symonds; H. Blairman & Sons; bought with the aid of a government grant and Philip Blairman who contributed half the cost 1945.   [16.1/45]

59 SET OF FOUR CHAIRS

*c.*1730–40
Walnut; beech, pine

Upholstered, curvilinear backs and seats; the hipped cabriole forelegs have scroll brackets, are carved on the knees with a conventional shell and leaf-drop motif within a raised border

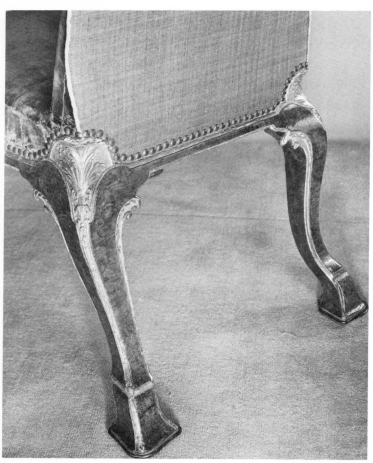

59

60 PAIR OF CHAIRS
*c.*1735–40
Walnut; oak

Pierced splat-backs styled with paired volutes and scrolled crestings; the cabriole front legs on claw and ball feet have shell and husk carving on the knees, with gadrooned brackets united by shaped seat rails centering on fronded scallop shells; oak-framed slip seats covered in Florentine carnation-pattern woolwork on a blue ground. The seat bases are incised 'III' and 'V'; the back rail of one chair is branded 'B'. H.96 (38); W.53 (21); D.43 (17).

Plugged joint slots cut into the rear posts and corresponding peg-holes on the side rails show that one specimen was converted into an armchair and the added members subsequently removed.

The cabriole legs relate in many points of detail to those on a suite of seat furniture which William Hallett supplied to Lord Irwin in 1735. C. G. Gilbert, 'Newly-Discovered Furniture by William Hallett', *Connoisseur*, Dec. 1964, pp. 224–5.

LIT: *L.A.C.*, No.60 (1967), p.10, fig.3.

PROV: Hugh Phillips; J. J. Wolff (Antiques); bequeathed by Frank Savery 1966.   [1.4/66]

and terminate in trifid feet; the covers are worked in half-stitch with a large arabesque design in red, white, and purple (faded to tan) wool, the canvas being drawn over the rails and secured by brass nails; red woollen backing fabric impressed with a glossy wave pattern (perhaps an example of 'harrateen'); silk nailing ribbon, curled hair stuffing, webbed bottom. Walnut legs, beech seat and back frame, the brackets reinforced with pine.
H.107 (42½); W.64 (25); D.59 (23).

The original suite consisted of a sofa and six single chairs the sofa is now in the Auckland Institute and Museum, New Zealand (*Antique Collector*, Feb. 1960, p.11, repr.); the other two chairs were acquired by Stair & Co., New York (*Connoisseur*, Jan. 1962, p.xlvii, repr.). The trifid feet lend some support to the notion that the suite is of Scottish origin.

LIT: *Country Life*, 19 Aug. 1916, p.211, repr.

EXH: Temple Newsam, *Furniture Upholstery*, 1973 (31).

PROV: The Stewart Mackenzie family, Brahan Castle, Ross-shire, Scotland; Brahan Castle sale about 1950; Cecil Millar (Antiques); Hotspur, Ltd; bought with the aid of a government grant 1961.   [5/61]

60

61 SET OF TWO ARM AND SIX SINGLE CHAIRS
By Giles Grendey, London
*c.*1735–40
Beech

Each chair has a slightly hollowed back with a flattened cresting, rounded shoulders, curved uprights and a solid vase-shaped splat set into a shoe of ogee design; the compass seats with front aprons and original split-cane panels are raised on cabriole forelegs ending in pad feet united to the splayed and turned back legs by side stretchers; high rear and serpentine medial stretchers; two chairs have broad bowed arms with scroll terminals on swept supports. The frames are lavishly enriched with slightly differing chinoiserie designs in gold and silver with black details on a scarlet japanned ground. The central splats portray oriental figures standing beneath umbrellas against a landscape of feathery trees, bordered by floral festoons and headed by an interlace design featuring pairs of birds, masks and arabesques; the uprights, arms and seats are ornamented with diaper and strapwork patterns while the shoulders and knees bear acanthus fronds; the aprons and front feet display shell motifs and other parts are lightly decorated with gilding.
Arm: H.113 (44¼); W.60 (23½); D.52 (20½).
Single: H.105 (41¾); W.52 (21½); D.48 (19).

Grendey's trade label inscribed 'GILES GRENDEY / *St John's Square, Clerkenwell,* / LONDON, / MAKES and Sells all Sorts of / CABINET GOODS, Chairs, / Tables, Glasses, &c.' is pasted beneath the seat rail of both arm and one single chair. Seven of the chairs also carry impressed or incised initials on the base of the splat and uprights just above seat level: the following marks (presumably used by individual chairmakers in Grendey's employ) occur in various combinations 'HW; EA; IT; MW'. Apprenticeship records kept by the Inland Revenue show that several craftsmen working for Grendey during the 1735–40 period possessed initials corresponding to the stamps.

Contemporary evidence that Giles Grendey was involved in the export trade is corroborated by this set of chairs which originally formed part of a very large suite of scarlet-japanned

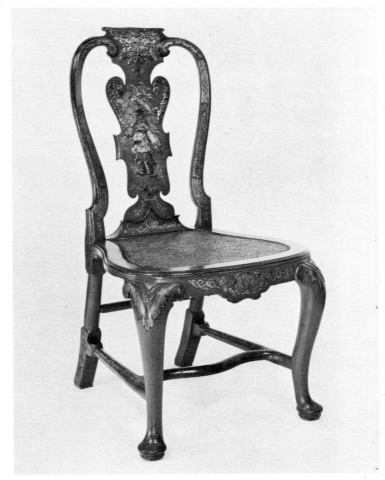

61

furniture supplied to the Duke of Infantado's castle at Lazcano, near San Sebastian in northern Spain. Furniture made in London for the Spanish market was specially styled to appeal to the Spaniard's taste for opulence. Accordingly these chairs display a maximum of flat surfaces for festive decorative treatment and moreover possess certain distinctly archaic features, such as high cabriole legs, stretchers and curved seats, typical of native Spanish furniture at the time.

A late nineteenth century photograph of the heavily furnished salon at Lazcano, reproduced in *La Casa del Infantado, cabeza de los Mendoza* by Cristina de Arteaga, Vol.II (Madrid, 1944), shows many pieces from this great suite in their original setting. The majority of items were purchased directly by Adolph Loewi in 1930 and removed to his shop in Venice. The firm's records reveal that he acquired seventy-two articles – fifty single and twelve armchairs; two day-beds; two pairs of mirrors; a pair of candlestands; a card table and a tripod tea table. The Spanish Art Gallery in London bought a labelled secretary separately from the Duke and a residue was apparently left at the castle. The present whereabouts of fifty-eight pieces is known and a comprehensive pictorial record of the various items was published in *Antiques* for April and December 1971. The suite is now widely dispersed, the following pieces being in public collections: twenty-four single and four armchairs together with two mirrors are owned by the Rosen Foundation, New York; the

61

61

Metropolitan Museum possesses an armchair and a card table; the V. & A. acquired a day-bed in 1938, the other going to the National Gallery of Victoria in 1946 and Temple Newsam House, Leeds purchased a pair of arm and six single chairs in 1970. Particulars of privately owned pieces are recorded in *Antiques*, April 1971 and Dec. 1971. Since then two more labelled armchairs and a second card table from the Hoyt collection have been acquired by French & Co., New York.

LIT: *Connoisseur*, June 1964, p.120; *L.A.C.*, No.66 (1970) p.3, repr.; *Collector's Guide*, Jan. 1971, p.68, repr. (colour); C. G. Gilbert, 'Furniture by Giles Grendey for the Spanish Trade', *Antiques*, April 1971, pp.544–550, repr; G. Wills, *English Furniture 1550–1760*, 1971, p.130, repr. (colour).

EXH: The remnant of a label on two chairs (intact version noted on a companion chair in London) records that they were shown at the first *Fiera Nazionale d'Arte Antica* at Cremona in 1937.

PROV: The Dukes of Infantado, Lazcano, Spain; bought in 1930 by Adolph Loewi (an American dealer operating from Venice); private collection in Italy; Pelham Galleries; H. Blairman & Sons, London; Neville Hamwee; bought with the aid of a government grant, a contribution from Mr & Mrs Neville Hamwee and the assistance of George Levy of Blairmans 1970. [10/70]

61

62

62 CHAIR
*c.*1730–50
Elm; pine

Curved back posts and top rail, vase-shaped splat with pierced heart, splayed slip seat; the front legs of bold cabriole form with high knees and pad feet, turned rear legs and stretchers; pegged joints, rear rail incised 'II'. Pine seat frame stuffed with hair and covered in leather.
H.97 (38½); W.56 (22); D.49 (19½).

The 'wild' figure on the splat may be an attempt by a country craftsman working in elm to match the striking decorative effects of walnut veneers used by fashionable chair makers. In remote districts the traditional 'Queen Anne' style lingered on until Chippendale's *Director* designs provided new inspiration for the ornamental elaboration of chair backs.

EXH: Temple Newsam, *Town & Country Furniture*, 1972 (3).

PROV: Bequeathed by Mrs Frank Gott, Weetwood Garth, Leeds 1941. [7.17/41]

TWENTY CHAIRS, gilt and needlework
By James Pascall, London, 1746
Under Cat. No.45 (illustrated)

63

63 CHAIR
*c.*1750
Mahogany

The pierced splat is profiled as a vase incorporating a lozenge, the interlacing strapwork system being worked in relief on the shaped cresting; the seat rails, styled with a corner moulding, centre on a pendant motif and the cabriole fore-legs, ending in claw and ball feet, are carved at the knee with acanthus volutes; slip seat. The back rail is incised 'VI'.
H.97 (38½); W.53 (21); D.46 (18).

PROV: Bequeathed by Frank Savery 1966.　　　[1.10/66]

64 CHAIR
*c.*1750
Mahogany; beech, pine

The moulded back posts, headed by prominent 'ears' carved with florets, support a shaped crest rail enriched with acanthus sprays; the interlacing strapwork splat incorporates a fronded crescent with rosette terminals; the angular cabriole legs ending in claw and ball feet are carved with formal acanthus ornament while the front rail has a gadrooned lower border; stump rear feet. Square seat recovered in floral needlework. Mahogany with a beech back rail and riven pine corner blocks, beech seat base.
H.95 (37½); W.55 (21¾); D.46 (18).

PROV: Bequeathed by Frank Savery 1966.　　　[1.9/66]

64

65 CHAIR
*c.*1750
Mahogany

The shaped crest rail raised on channelled back posts is carved with acanthus foliage and paired florets, while the interlacing strapwork splat centres on a crescent styled in the same manner. The seat frame, fronted by a gadrooned

65

moulding attached with nails, is supported on cabriole forelegs enriched at the knee with fronds and ending in claw and ball feet. The slip seat re-covered in old floral needlework on a blue ground.
H.94 (37); W.53 (21); D.44 (17½).

A very common chair pattern, although not featured in design books of the period. The claw and ball foot had become unfashionable by the time Chippendale published his *Director* in 1754.

PROV: W. H. Cliff, Farnley; bequeathed by Sir George Martin 1976. [51.20/76]

66 ARMCHAIR

*c.*1750
Mahogany

Of virtually identical pattern but inferior in quality to Cat. No.65 and with orthodox scrolled arms on raked supports. Slip seat covered in modern needlework.
H.95 (37½); W.60 (23½); D.51 (20).

PROV: John Bell (Antiques) Aberdeen; bequeathed by Sir George Martin 1976. [51.21/76]

67 ARMCHAIR

*c.*1750
Mahogany; beech

Almost identical in design to Cat. No.66 but with a stuffed-over seat, the outward-curving arms and supports enriched with channelling. Re-railed and heavily restored; modern upholstery.
H.97 (38½); W.62 (24½); D.53 (21).

EXH: Temple Newsam, *L.A.C.F. Members Exhibition*, 1952 (253).

PROV: Auctioned by Renton & Renton, Harrogate, 16 Sept. 1954, lot 799; bequeathed by Sir George Martin 1976.
[51.19/76]

68 CHAIR

*c.*1750–60
Mahogany; beech

The moulded back posts terminate in volutes carved with lively rococo foliage and acorns, while the serpentine crest

68

rail features an oak cluster suspended from ribbons; the open vase-shaped splat composed of interlacing straps and scrolls carved with acanthus fronds centres on an open lozenge; the cabriole front legs on claw and ball feet are enriched with clusters of oak leaves and acorns tied by ribbons, stump rear feet. Mahogany, with beech side and front rails, corner braces replaced by blocks.
H.96 (38); W.59 (23); D.51 (20).

A small table with cabriole legs of identical pattern is recorded.

PROV: Lotherton Hall; the Gascoigne gift 1970.   [42/70]

69 SET OF FOUR ARMCHAIRS
*c.*1755
Mahogany; beech

Rectangular hollow seats on straight front and splayed rear legs with fretted corner brackets; the curvilinear arms have pierced frond-carved elbows and border scrolls; the slightly flared backs with shaped top-rails are filled with lattice work in the Chinese taste centering on open foliate panels; the crestings, delicately carved with acanthus fronds terminating in short husk pendants feature an heraldic device 'out of a ducal coronet a demi-griffin segreant' – the crest of the Connock family. Mahogany with beech seat rails and corner braces; the blocked feet and brass castors with friction rollers date from about 1840.
H.95 (37½); W.57 (22½); D.51 (20).

Thomas Chippendale stated that 'Chairs after the Chinese manner are very proper for a Lady's Dressing Room: especially if it is hung with India Paper' and remarked that the style 'admits of the greatest variety'. Most contemporary pattern books illustrate chairs in the Chinese taste, but this set does not relate to any published design, although a suite at Firle Place and an example formerly at Bramshill (V. & A. W.46–1962) offer close analogies, the latter being almost certainly from the same workshop.

LIT (only the principal references are cited): *Country Life*, 12 March 1904, p.378; Mallett & Son, *Catalogue of Antiques*, 1936, repr.; *Apollo*, Sept. 1936, p.145, repr. & p.152; *Apollo*, Oct. 1947, p.81, repr.; *L.A.C.*, No.46–7 (1961), pp.16–19, repr.; A. Coleridge, *Chippendale Furniture*, 1968, p.134; *Octagon*, Vol.XII, (Spring 1975), pp.14–15, repr.

EXH: London, V. & A., *B.A.D.A. Golden Jubilee*, 1968 (144) pl.105.

PROV: The original set of at least eight passed by descent from Nicholas Connock of Treworgey Manor, Cornwall to William Connock Marshall; acquired during the 1930s by Sellick (Antiques) Exeter and about 1935 by Mallett & Son after which point the frequent changes of ownership and splitting of the suite become increasingly difficult to unravel. In 1947 Malletts sold four to Commander Clark two of which were purchased by Spink (1975), and passed via Malletts to a private collector. A pair which F. Partridge & Sons bought from Mrs Soames in 1944 were sold to Viscount Downe, Wykeham Abbey, Yorkshire; the four now at Temple Newsam were obtained by H. Blairman & Sons from an American source; bought with the aid of a government grant 1960. [24/60]

69

70 ARMCHAIR
c.1755–65
Mahogany; beech

Of rectangular design, the solid upholstered back and seat covered in modern figured velvet. The shaped arms, filled with an open system of Chinese lattice paling, centre on an octagonal panel while the square front supports are enriched with a complex pattern of blind frets; the legs, united by plain side, rear and medial stretchers are headed by pierced spandrel brackets. Beech seat rails.
H.95 (37½); W.60 (23½); D.57 (22½).

PROV: Bequeathed by Frank Savery 1966. [1.16/66]

70

71 MASTER'S ARMCHAIR
c.1755
Mahogany, parcel gilt; elm

The high back is vigorously carved with a fantastic open design of arches and fronded scrolls in the rococo, gothic and Chinese tastes. The composition incorporates various emblems: clasped hands set between a pair of leafy pagoda-capped columns, entwined snakes, two doves and olive sprays; the knotted uprights are outlined with long C-scrolls and embellished with floral festoons; the cresting, bordered with flamework, centres on an oak spray, and the bowed arms terminating in monster heads and curved supports are enriched with acanthus; the scrolling seat rails carved with flame borders centre at the front on a bouquet of roses and wheat ears; the wyvern forelegs rest on octagonal pads and the cabriole rear legs end in shells. The back is mainly of laminated construction braced with iron ties; elm rails and corner struts faced with parcel gilt mahogany; empty mortice

slots and breaks show that various ornamental elements have been lost; the seat re-covered in green leather.
H.128 (50½); W.69 (27); D.54 (21½).

The date and possible authorship of this chair is suggested by stylistic analogies with a fantastic Masters' armchair made by Edward Newman for the Joiners' Company in 1754 (*D.E.F.*, I, p.283, fig.118).

The general symbolic significance of the emblems suggests it was made for a fellowship society or possibly to commemorate a marriage alliance. The pair of joined hands, the two doves and olive sprays are common symbols of Concord and Friendship; the intertwined serpents joined at the mouth are also emblematic of Peace; the twin columns represent Stability and the rose and wheat might symbolize Love and Fertility; the wyverns and oak sprig may be heraldic but seem to possess no more than decorative significance.

EXH: Brighton Art Gallery, *Follies and Fantasies*, Aug. 1971 (248).

PROV: By descent to Sir Hugh Cholmeley, Easton Hall, Lincs; Christie's, 15 July 1948, lot 147; J. Ross; bought 1957. [23/57]

72

72 ARMCHAIR
*c.*1755
Mahogany; oak

Curvilinear, gothic-pattern splat, the tracery carved with acanthus fronds, C-scrolls and flame borders in the rococo taste, the top rail, arms and keeled cabriole legs on knurl feet enriched with similar motifs; upholstered in Berlin woolwork portraying a bird in a tree within a floral cartouche on a brown ground. The arms, added at a later date, disfigure the proportions of this chair. Mahogany frame with oak rails.
H.100 (39½); W.56 (22); D.47 (18½).

The back corresponds exactly to the left-hand design on pl. xv of Thomas Chippendale's *Director*, 1754 and the legs are also based on this design (which was omitted from the 1762 edition). In the prefatory notes Chippendale refers to this plate as featuring 'new-pattern Chairs, which, if executed according to their Designs by a skillful workman, will have a very good effect' and mentions that some of the ornaments 'can be omitted at pleasure'. The frame conforms precisely to the dimensions specified in the notes.

The timber and craftsmanship of this chair are not of particularly high quality, indicating a provincial origin; it is therefore an interesting example of how Chippendale's *Director* influenced contemporary furniture makers who lacked the training and ability to produce their own designs.

PROV: Miss E. K. Emsley, Boston Spa, Yorkshire; auctioned by Hollis & Webb, Leeds, 19 March 1963, lot 125; given by Sir George Martin 1972. [1/72]

72

73 CHAIR
c.1755–60
Mahogany; beech

The vigorously bowed, frond-carved cresting is combined with a vase-shaped back splat boldly pierced in the gothic taste and edged with an acanthus fringe; ribbon and rosette shoe moulding. The seat is supported on straight chamfered front legs enriched with blind gothic frets and raked rear legs interconnected by a system of elaborately pierced stretchers; ornamental C-scroll corner brackets at the front and sides; stuffed-over seat. Beech rails and corner braces, modern seat cover.
H.94 (37); W.57 (22½); D.48 (19).

An identical chair from the Coppinger Prichard collection is illustrated in *D.E.F.*, I, p.279, fig.165.

PROV: Bought from the Harding Fund 1938.   [26/38]

carved with flame-bordered C-scrolls and fronds; open splat of traceried vase design embellished with rococo details and headed by a pierced cabochon motif; the straight front legs and slightly splayed slip seat are enhanced with a simple corner moulding; fretwork brackets; side, rear and medial stretchers. The beech seat frames upholstered in modern green damask, are incised 'II' and 'III', the back rails 'I' and 'II'.
H.95 (37¾); W.54 (21½); D.46 (18).

The splat corresponds to a design which figures twice in the third edition of Chippendale's *Director*, pl. xiii (right) dated 1761 and pl. xiv (right) dated 1753. It was his most frequently copied chair pattern.

LIT: C. G. Gilbert, *L.G. & R.F.*, 1972, p.10, repr.

EXH: Temple Newsam House, *Thomas Chippendale*, 1951 (126)

PROV: Albert Amor (Antiques); bought 1940.
                                        [15.1 & 2/40]

73

74 PAIR OF CHAIRS
c.1755–65
Mahogany; beech

Slightly flared back, the channelled uprights enriched with a spine of alternating rolls and beads, the shaped top rail is

74

74

75

75 PAIR OF CHAIRS
*c.*1755–65
Mahogany; oak, pine

The back posts, cresting and splat are bordered by shallow C-scrolls, fronded top rail, interlaced splat of flowing tracer-ied design the straps 'stitched' and embellished with acanthus plumes; square grooved front legs, plain at the rear, side and medial stretchers. Oak rails and corner struts, pine glue-blocks, pegged construction, the stuffed-over seat covered in modern fabric.
H.96 (38); W.56 (22); D.44 (17½).

PROV: H. C. Foot (Antiques); bought 1939.   [4.1 & 2/39]

76 ARMCHAIR
*c.*1755–60
Mahogany; beech

The well raked upholstered back, padded arms and serpentine-

fronted seat are stuffed and covered in floral tapestry woven in coloured wool and silks on a linen warp with a blue-grey ground; shaped seat rails enriched with fronded border scrolls and diaper patterns centering at the front on a shell, the cabriole forelegs, carved with rococo shells and foliage, end in hoof and pad feet, plain rear cabrioles, the arm sup-ports and knurl elbows decorated with acanthus sprays. Solid mahogany with beech corner struts and inner frame-work. The skilfully shaded tapestry back and seat panels of matched design, were probably woven at Beauvais in the late eighteenth century; repaired areas and nail-head marks show they originally covered another suite.
H.96 (38); W.72 (28½); D.69 (27).

In the prefatory notes to his *Director* Thomas Chippendale observed that 'both the Backs and Seats' of such chairs 'must be covered with Tapestry, or other sort of Needlework'. Two 'French Elbow Chairs' of equivalent design covered with strikingly similar floral tapestry are illustrated by F. Lewis Hinckley, *Directory of Queen Anne, Early Georgian and Chippen-dale Furniture*, 1971, pl.122.

LIT: *L.A.C.*, No.20 (1953) p.8, repr.

EXH: Temple Newsam, *Thomas Chippendale*, 1951 (82).

PROV: Alfred Jowett; bought 1952.   [32/52]

76

77

77 PAIR OF ARMCHAIRS

*c.*1755–60
Mahogany; beech, oak

The shaped backs, seats and arm-pads are upholstered in contemporary *gros-point* (cross-stitch) needlework worked in wool and silk with a broad design of palmettes and arabesques in various shades of red on a yellow ground, restuffed and secured by brass-headed nails; the cabriole forelegs and knurl feet are ornamented with fronded cabochon motifs, plain rear cabrioles on club feet; the curvilinear, slightly channelled seat rails styled with rococo scrolls, incised lines and gadrooning centre on acanthus sprays; twisted scroll-over elbows with frond enrichment; the dished feet conceal brass castors with leather rollers. Beech back frame and seat rails faced with mahogany, oak corner struts.
H.100 (39½); W.69 (27); D.64 (25).

Many designs for armchairs of this form occur in contemporary pattern books where they are termed 'French Chairs'. Chippendale remarked 'Both the Backs and Seats must be covered with Tapestry, or other sort of Needlework' and advised the covers be 'nailed with Brass Nails'.

PROV: Given by Mrs A Cooke, in memory of her husband Alf Cooke and her son Lt. Alfred Cooke 1965.   [3.2/65]

78

78 PAIR OF ARMCHAIRS
*c.*1755–60
Mahogany; beech

The rectangular backs, seats and arm-rests are upholstered in needlework stuffed over the rails and nailed through a woven band; cabriole forelegs carved with clusters of grapes, vine leaves and tendrils on claw and ball feet, the rear cabrioles are plain, terminating in pad feet; swept arm supports the scroll-over elbows enriched with floret and frond motifs, the dished feet conceal brass castors with leather rollers. The *petit-point* covers, worked in coloured wools and silk depict garden flowers on a dark-blue ground surrounding circular pictorial panels, those on the seats portray mountainous landscapes inhabited by birds, rabbits, sheep and deer and the backs display biblical subjects: Hagar and Ishmael in the Wilderness; Jacob wrestling with the Angel. The needlework is contemporary with, but not original to, the frames; a photograph published in 1931 shows one of the chairs upholstered in cut velvet. Mahogany, with beech rails, back and corner braces.
H.96 (38); W.69 (27); D.66 (26).

The struggling figures of Jacob wrestling with the Angel are taken from a large folio with double-page engravings: *Historiae Sacrae Veteris et Novi Testamenti* published in Amsterdam by Nicholas Visscher about 1660 with engravings after various artists.

78

78

78

LIT: *Apollo*, July 1931, p.25, fig.xi; *L.A.C.*, No.39 (1958), p.22, fig.12; M. Swain, 'Pictorial Chair Covers: Some Engraved Sources', *Furniture History*, XI (1975), p.80, pls.173–4.

PROV: Lord Plender of Sundridge; H. Blairman & Sons; Lady Burton; given by Barbara Karmel, Arnold, Raymond and Stanley Burton 1966.   [24/66]

79 PAIR OF CHAIRS

*c.*1760
Mahogany; beech

The back posts are simply styled as pilasters headed by fronds with a bowed top rail; the traceried splat which rises from a brass moulding is composed of faceted columns forming pointed arches ornamented with C-scrolls and acanthus; the dished seat rails, carved with rosettes and leaf-drops, are supported on triple column front legs clustered in the gothic style but with Ionic capitals; shaped feet carved in the rococo taste; the frames are inlaid with brass strings, grooves and reeding. Beech corner blocks and slip seats (re-covered); one chair fitted with later castors.
H.96 (38); W.54 (21½); D.44 (17½).

79

A small group of mid eighteenth century brass-inlaid furniture loosely associated with the workshop of John Channon has been identified; the decorative technique was not widely popular at this time and probably restricted to a few firms, but these chairs are not closely allied to any published examples.

LIT: *Antiques*, May 1969, p.687, fig.10; G. Wills, *English Furniture 1760–1900*, 1971, p.56, pl.43; C. G. Gilbert, *L.G. & R.F.*, 1972, p.22, repr.

EXH: Temple Newsam, *Thomas Chippendale*, 1951 (98).

PROV: By descent from Robert Reid, Moor Park, Harrogate to his daughter the Hon. Mrs J. de Courcy; bought 1963.
                    [12/63]

80 CHAIR

*c.*1760–65
Mahogany; beech

The slightly flared back posts surmounted by a shaped cresting outlined with scrolls, frame a vase-pattern splat of cusped tracery design, headed by a flamework C-scroll and husk-drop motif; the stuffed-over seat is raised on square chamfered legs connected by side, medial and rear bar stretchers. Beech rails and front corner struts, back rail renewed.
H.94 (37); W.59 (23); D.49 (19½).

PROV: Bought 1939.   [7/39]

81 CHAIR

*c.*1760–65
Mahogany; beech

The flared ladder-back has a serpentine crest rail and rungs of open interlaced design carved with acanthus fronds; serpentine-fronted seat stuffed over the rails and covered in modern damask; straight chamfered forelegs with corner mouldings, side, medial and rear stretchers. Beech seat with one original corner brace, the rear rail re-veneered and lightly incised 'I W'; the first and third rungs are modern reproductions.
H.94 (37); W.56 (22); D.46 (18).

PROV: Bequeathed by Frank Savery 1966.   [1.13/66]

82 CHAIR

*c.*1760–70
Mahogany; beech

Of ladder-back design with a slightly hollowed back; the serpentine crest rail and three rungs styled with scroll profiles, are pierced in the gothic taste with cusps, quatrafoils

81

82

and mouchette tracery; the hollow seat, covered in calf leather, is raised on square chamfered legs united by side, medial and rear stretchers; the spandrel brackets missing.
H.97 (38½); W.59 (23); D.49 (19½).

PROV: By descent to Mrs Florence Bird; given 1964.   [1/64]

FOUR ARMCHAIRS, gilt and tapestry
By Fell and Turton, London, 1771
Under Cat. No.46 (illustrated)

83 PAIR OF ARMCHAIRS
*c.*1780
Mahogany

Oval, slightly hollowed backs with pearl-beaded and mould-ed surrounds framing three upright splats carved with oval rosette paterae; channelled, gracefully wrythen arms and supports with circular elbow paterae; serpentine-fronted compass seats with fluted rails, square tapered and grooved front legs on spade feet, splayed rear legs rising to brace the back; seat covered in modern green leather secured by nails,

beech corner blocks added.
H.97 (38½); W.57 (22½); D.48 (19).

Delicately proportioned chairs with backs of very similar design exist – a fine example is illustrated *D.E.F.*, I, p.299, fig.233.

LIT: *L.A.C.*, No.9 (1967) p.9, fig.2.

PROV: Bequeathed by Frank Savery 1966.   [1.6/66]

84 ARMCHAIR
*c.*1780–85
Mahogany; beech

The oval upholstered back is framed by a waterleaf moulding and the compass fronted seat, faced with reeding, centres on a tablet of swag drapery; the tapering reeded legs are styled with lotus leaf bands and headed by panels carved at the front corners with drapery swags; the padded arms carved with foliate scrolls rest on channelled supports which curve down to join the rear uprights – an uncommon design feature; castors missing.
H.91 (30); W.60 (23½); D.51 (20).

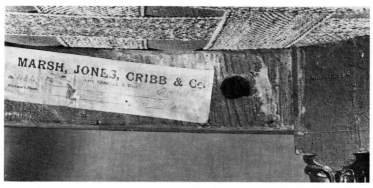

84

The beech seat rails are drilled inside to receive cramps when gluing the joints, one rear leg is stamped 'H. W. COOPER' and the underframe carries a printed label – 'MARSH, JONES, CRIBB & Co / (LATE KENDELL & Co)' with the date 'Oct. 1907' a number '46681' and workman's name (illegible) written in pencil. The impressed name is perhaps an unidentified maker's mark, but the paper label was put on by the well known Leeds furnishers who sold the chair from their antiques department.

PROV: Recorded by Sam Wilson as having been bought from Marsh, Jones & Cribb of Leeds in May 1908 and entered in his notebook as 'A very fine Hepplewhite Arm chair 15.15.0 re-covering and doing up 7.0.0; the Sam Wilson Bequest 1925. [S.W.215]

85 PAIR OF CHAIRS

*c.*1785
Mahogany; beech

The moulded hoop backs frame pierced vase-shaped splats fashioned of five lotus columns enriched with anthemion plumes, guilloche bands and pearl beading. The cresting is composed of three wheat sheafs which protrude from the lip of the vase and the shoulders are carved with husk chains suspended from florets. The gently curved seats are raised on square, slightly hollowed front legs decorated with husk pendants, headed by lotus capitals and splayed at the base. Beech seat rails and corner bars, the back rail of each is impressed twice with a strange mark.
H.94 (37); W.57 (22¼); D.49 (19½).

EXH: Temple Newsam, *L.A.C.F. Members Exhibition*, 1952 (256).

PROV: Lord Moynihan, Carr Manor, Leeds; Carr Manor sale 30 Nov.–3 Dec. 1937 (Hollis & Webb, Leeds), lot 291; bequeathed by Sir George Martin 1976. [51.17/76]

84

85

86 SET OF SIX SINGLE AND ONE ARMCHAIR
*c.*1785
Mahogany; elm

The moulded shield-shaped backs are designed with straight top rails, carved leaf fans at the base and five hollowed banister splats enriched with husk chains; the straight front legs with channelled outer faces support bowed seats stuffed over the rails and covered in leather; serpentine moulded arms; elm seat rails braced at the front corners; side, rear and medial stretchers.
H.90 (35½); W.54 (21½); D.47 (18½).

PROV: Agnes and Norman Lupton Bequest 1953.
[13.369/53]

87

86

87 SET OF ONE ARM AND FIVE SINGLE CHAIRS
*c.*1785–90
Mahogany; pine

The moulded shield-shaped backs enclose lyre splats composed of five central 'strings' flanked by upright S-scrolls headed by lotus fan and floret terminals suspending a laurel loop; the 'strings' extend between rosette studs carved on the arched crest rail and pedestal shoe; the elbow chair has curved arms on swept supports. The serpentine-fronted slip seats with rounded sides are raised on straight tapered forelegs with corner mouldings connected by side, medial and rear stretcher bars; corner blocks and angle braces added later.
H.95 (37½); W.51 (20); D.46 (18); armchair: W.53 (21); D.48 (19).

The pine seat bases covered in modern fabric are branded 'H', the bases and frames are incised with Roman numerals ranging between I and XII indicating the set was originally larger.

A pair of arm and four slightly variant single chairs with backs of almost identical pattern are illustrated in *Apollo*, Sept. 1952, p. xxii (trade advertisement of Gregory & Co). Other comparable sets are recorded.

PROV: The Gascoigne gift 1970.
[39/70]

88 CHAIR

*c.*1785–90
Mahogany; beech

The shield-shaped back, enriched with corner mouldings, frames a splat composed of branching tracery with a central rosette patera surmounted by three plumes beneath a canopy; the main ribs are carved with husk drops and the back posts have low fluted caps. The dipped, slightly bowed seat is raised on square moulded front legs with splayed toes. Mahogany frame, beech seat rails and corner struts, the back rail impressed '1661'.
H.94 (37); W.52 (20½); D.44 (17½).

PROV: Leonard Knight, Ltd; bequeathed by Frank Savery 1966.   [1.12/66]

89

88

89 PAIR OF CHAIRS

*c.*1790–95
Mahogany; beech

Square back with swept shoulders, the central splat of fluted vase design rises from a lotus foot and is headed by Prince of

Wales feathers; the side splats and top and bottom rails are styled as a frame for the central member; slightly curved back and seat; straight channelled front legs with side and medial stretchers. The seat stuffed with hair between layers of canvas supported on webbing with a linen interfacing, covered in red Morocco leather secured by two rows of brass studs; beech rails and corner braces; incised underneath 'III' and 'V'.
H.90 (35½); W.52 (20½); D44 (17½).

The finely carved back is based on a design in George Hepplewhite's *Guide*, pl.i. The retention of stretchers and the history of these chairs suggests a provincial origin.

EXH: Leeds Art Gallery, *English Furniture*, 1930 (118 & 120); Temple Newsam, *Furniture Upholstery*, 1973 (27).

PROV: Both chairs carry a paper label inscribed in ink 'This chair is the property / of my Great Nephew / Frank Gott / Jan. 24th 1881 C. A. MacBraire' and a note amongst the Gott papers at Leeds University records that they were formerly part of a set of 12 chairs and a settee belonging to to Mrs William Rhodes who moved from Wentbridge to

90

91 ARMCHAIR
*c.*1790–1800
Mahogany; oak, pine

Rounded back with pierced, vase-shaped splat, the open pattern crossed by a fluted band; curved arms, slip seat raised on square tapered front legs united to the rear uprights by stretchers. Oak back rail, pine corner blocks and seat frame stuffed with hair and covered in modern fabric. The underside incised 'V' (twice).
H.96 (38); W.54 (21½); D.44 (17½).

The pedestrian quality and existence of stretchers implies a provincial origin; stylistically Cat. No.91 is closer to Hepplewhite's chair designs (1788) than those in Sheraton's *Drawing-Book* (1791–4).

PROV: Agnes and Norman Lupton Bequest 1953.
[13.379/53]

Armley House, Leeds in 1803; they passed to her daughter Abigail and she left them to her niece Caroline Abigail MacBraire who distributed them to members of the family. Frank Gott commissioned four copies to make himself up a set of six chairs; bequeathed by Mrs Frank Gott, Weetwood Garth, Leeds 1941.   [7.13 & 14/41]

90 SET OF SIX CHAIRS
*c.*1790–95
Mahogany; beech

Each with a hoop-back; the surround and splat, composed of three bifurcated ribs, slightly dished and headed by a floret and husk device; hollow seat stuffed over the rails and covered with modern fabric, supported at the front on turned peg-legs carved with a collar of waterleaf. Mahogany with beech seat rails and corner braces.
H.92 (36½); W.51 (20); D.48 (18¾).

PROV: Agnes and Norman Lupton Bequest 1953.
[13.390/53]

92

92 PAIR OF CHAIRS

*c.*1790–1800
Mahogany; beech

The square backs, outlined with a hollow moulding, have seven reeded banisters headed by waterleaf capitals, a central tablet and stay rail; the compass seats with swept sides are raised on straight moulded front and splayed rear legs united by plain side, medial and rear stretchers; beech seat rails braced at the front by corner bars, stuffed with hay and tow supported by the original webbing, modern covers. The back rails are impressed underneath 'IW'.
H.87 (34½); W.51 (20); D.43 (17).

PROV: Agnes and Norman Lupton Bequest 1953

[13.385/53]

93 SET OF EIGHTEEN HALL CHAIRS

*c.*1800
Mahogany

93

Solid back profiled as a classical urn, slightly splayed forward sloping dipped seat having roll-over sides faced with paterae; flat X-shaped front legs connected by a broad stretcher to rear fork, the terminal joints masked by circular paterae, the back panel and rear support braced by a wedge-shaped strut, additional strength supplied by iron straps. The backs are painted with the initials 'F I' below a Viscount's coronet in gilt with green, red, black, and white details – for Frances, widow of the 9th Viscount Irwin, owner of Temple Newsam 1778–1807. She probably bought this set of chairs for the Great Hall following extensive remodelling of the south wing in 1796. Several are in a damaged state.
H.105 (41½); W.52 (20½); D.40 (16).

Sheraton's *Cabinet Dictionary* (1803), p.250 contains a lucid definition of Hall Chairs '. . . are such as are placed in halls, for the use of servants or strangers waiting on business. They are generally made all of mahogany . . . and the crest or arms of the family painted on the centre of the back'. Four chairs of identical pattern were auctioned by J. E. Tennant, Richmond, Yorkshire, 20 July 1977, lot 190, repr.

LIT: *Furniture History*, III (1967), p.16 and p.26.

EXH: *Temple Newsam Heirlooms*, 1972 (31).

PROV: The chairs are recorded in the Temple Newsam inventory of 1808 (Y.A.S. Library DD.54) '4th Room Great Hall Ground Floor – 18 mahogany hall chairs with hollow backs and seats'; given by the Earl of Halifax 1922.
[1922/F.14]

94 GARDEN CHAIR

Late 18th century
Wrought iron

The rectangular slatted seat with a central brace is raised on straight legs united by H-pattern stretchers and ending in circular pad feet; the back is of pointed arch design with lancet tracery and a quatrafoil in the apex; upward curving arms with continuous supports ending in scrolls. The main members are fashioned of flat, slightly rounded iron bars united by rivets, the front rail and stretchers are constructed of rods. Traces of dark green paint.
H.90 (35½); W.42 (16½); D.37 (14½).

A microscopic examination of paint samples on a companion chair acquired by the V & A (W.11–1977) reveals thirty-five distinct layers. The frame was painted green seventeen times, white eight times, brown four times, grey three times. The original coat was grass green. These chairs are from the only known suite of English late-Georgian iron garden furniture. An identical pair is illustrated by B. Reade, *Regency Antiques*, 1953, pl.97. Windsor chairs which commonly served out of doors were often painted green.

PROV: Acquired by Jellinek and Sampson, Ltd in the Cotswolds; bought from the Harding Fund 1977. [1/77]

94

95 PAIR OF ARMCHAIRS
c.1800–05
Beech

The frames are japanned black and outlined with white lines enclosing variously coloured painted decoration on the principal surfaces. The square backs contain stylized lyre splats enriched at the base with a flaming urn flanked by griffins; the turned top rails centre on rounded tablets painted with garden flowers and the circular seat frames are ornamented with classical foliage. The high arms merge with turned supports resting on blocks and the slightly splayed ring-turned front legs are headed by lotus rosettes; the seats re-caned.
H.87 (34½); W.53 (21); D.48 (19).

Each seat rail is impressed underneath with a large letter 'G' enclosing a smaller 'J' and the initials 'IT' alongside.

Three closely similar sets of early Regency chairs bearing the same mark have been recorded, one set was sold by Sotheby's, 13 May 1966, lot 139, repr.

PROV: Theda, Lady Nussey, Little Rushwood, Sutton Howgrave, nr. Ripon, Yorkshire; Little Rushwood sale 18–19 July 1962 (Renton & Renton, Harrogate) lot 713; bequeathed by Sir George Martin 1976.   [51.15/76]

95

DINING CHAIR, mahogany
By Gillows, Lancaster, 1810
Under Cat. No.495 (illustrated)

PAIR OF CURRICLE CHAIRS, rosewood
By Gillows, Lancaster, *c*.1811
Under Cat. No.508 (illustrated)

ARM AND FOUR SINGLE CHAIRS, mahogany
By Gillows, Lancaster, *c*.1825
Under Cat. No.509 (illustrated)

96 PAIR OF CHAIRS

Made by Morel and Seddon, London to the design of A. W. N. Pugin
1828
Rosewood; mahogany, beech, oak

VR BP   Nº187   1866

⅓ actual size

The rectangular rosewood frames, richly styled with sunk gothic panels, gilt mouldings and ormolu mounts, support loose padded backs and seat bases raised on straight faceted front legs; the rear legs and back posts designed with side spandrels, are faced with recessed gothic panels outlined in gilt and the seat rails, bordered by gilt mouldings, are embellished with seventeen back-pinned ormolu tablets of various foliate and floral patterns; the curved top rail, mounted with a pierced vine-trail is capped by circular bosses; the backs are supported behind by open parcel-gilt tracery headed by a wavy band; gilt-brass castors. Part solid and part veneered rosewood frames, the inner structures are built of mahogany, beech and oak. Re-upholstered in modern crimson velvet, pieces of the original red silk damask are visible behind the top rail.
H.100 (39½); W.59 (23); D.56 (22).

The seat rail of one chair is branded 'WINDSOR CASTLE ROOM 510' with a crown between the letters 'VR', the date '1866' and a second smaller crown; the other chair is stamped 'VR BP No 187 1866'. Various inscriptions occur on the chassis of the loose backs and seats and on the frames behind them. One is marked in pencil 'Ths Hoare', 'No 3' and 'B & D' and in ink 'Thos Hoare' (twice), 'WM' and 'No 21'; the companion is signed 'Thomson No 2' (twice), 'Rosier' (twice) and 'T. Sheppard' (twice). These names, which presumably belong to craftsmen employed by Morel & Seddon, are found on other chairs from the same set. G. de Bellaigue (q.v.) records one inscribed 'Thomson 1828'. Several of the ormolu mounts bear impressed numbers, e.g. 6, 5, 11, 18 etc.

The chairs were designed by A. W. N. Pugin for the dining

96

room at Windsor Castle and are recorded in Morel & Seddon's Estimate '48 dining room chairs (annotated in pencil 'query if 36') ornamented and gilt frames as designed, the backs and seats stuffed and covered with Office silk and trimmed with silk gimp, lace, fringe etc'. The 'Crimson Figured Damask' for the curtains and upholstery, costing 19/- a yard was supplied by the King, the material being made up by Morel & Seddon who provided the 'Office silk' lining and trimmings.

Two armchairs *en suite* and other dining room furniture of a similar sophisticated gothic character was commissioned at the same time. Apparently only thirty-six dining chairs and not the forty-eight originally contemplated were ordered. At least twelve were removed to the Throne Room at Buckingham Palace prior to 1866. Nine have been dispersed and apart from this pair are now in various private collections.

LIT: *Connoisseur*, June 1964, p.76, pl.3; *L.A.C.*, No.71 (1972) p.3, fig.1; Geoffrey de Bellaigue and Pat Kirkham, 'George IV and the Furnishing of Windsor Castle', *Furniture History*, VIII (1972) pp.2–34, pl.7; (documentation and archive references quoted pp.14–16 & p.26).

PROV: George IV Windsor Castle; purchased about 1960 by H. Blairman & Sons; John Aspinall, 44 Berkeley Square, London; bought with the aid of a government grant 1972.
[23/72]

SEVEN CHAIRS, elm
By Atkinson & Barker, Leeds, 1846
Under Cat. No.537 (illustrated)

97 PAIR OF CHAIRS
c.1860
Birch finished to simulate papier-mâché

Of 'crown back' design with knuckles at the base; the rounded seats, partly stuffed over the rails, are covered in contemporary Berlin woolwork; turned, slightly splayed front legs joined by an ornamental stretcher, plain side and rear stretcher rods. The frames are coated with black papier-mâché decorated with Chinese garden scenes and floral sprays in pearl shell with gilt details.
H.82 (32½); W.38 (15); D.38 (15).

The term 'crown back' is used for this pattern in a chair catalogue issued by William Collins & Son of High Wycombe in 1872. See J. Gloag, 'The Nomenclature of mid-Victorian Chairs', *Connoisseur*, August 1968, pp.233–6.

PROV: Purchased in Cornwall about 1945; bequeathed by Sir George Martin 1976.
[51.26/76]

98 FOUR DRAWING ROOM CHAIRS
Attributed to Thomas Mills, Bradford
c.1850–60
Walnut; beech

Moulded balloon backs with ornamental openwork splats centering on florets; shaped seats stuffed with hair and covered in the original green velvet secured by braid; hipped cabriole front legs on pointed toes. Walnut frames with beech seat rails and corner blocks.
H.89 (35); W.44 (17½); D.40 (16).

Three chairs of identical design in a private house near Bradford bear the label 'FROM THOMAS MILLS / CABINET AND UPHOLSTERY WAREHOUSE / MARKET STREET BRADFORD'. According to entries in local *Trade Directories* this firm was founded *c*.1836 and occupied premises at No.61 and later No.45, Market Street, the business being recorded in 1845 as 'cabinet maker, upholsterer, paper hanger, carver, gilder and feather merchant'. About 1862 Backhouse was taken into partnership and after 1875 the firm is listed as Charles Mills & Co at various addresses in central Bradford until it closed down in 1896 or 97.

PROV: Given by C. A. Andrews 1930   [1930/F1]

98, 99

99 ROCKING CHAIR
Attributed to Thomas Mills, Bradford
Walnut; beech
*c.*1850–60

Moulded cameo back with floral cresting, braced to the seat by corner scrolls; hipped cabriole front legs with floral carving and scroll toes mounted on rockers; solid buttoned back and sprung seat stuffed with hair and flock, covered in the original green velvet secured with braid. The rockers added later. Walnut frame with beech seat rails.
H.95 (37½); W.59 (23); D.56 (22).

En suite with the preceding set of chairs. Drawing room suites generally consisted of seven or nine pieces – a couch, two easy chairs, four or six single chairs and possibly a pair of foot stools.

PROV: Given by C. A. Andrews 1930.   [1930/F2]

100 ARMCHAIR
1864
Oak

The high upholstered back has an arched cresting enriched with zig-zag and dog-tooth borders; the lunette centres on a raised shield inlaid with the monogram 'WSJ' in ivory beneath an heraldic crest of 'a rayed sun between two branches in orle' with the motto '*in deo spes nostra*' (in God is our Hope) carved in black letter script below and the date 'AD 1864'. The straight arms with knurled foliate elbows rest on moulded X-framed supports, the spandrels and legs, of cusped arch design being lavishly carved with foliated drop tracery on a stippled ground. The solid back and loose seat are covered in machined verdure tapestry fixed with faceted nail heads. The castors are impressed 'COPE'S PATENT'.
H.112 (44); W.59 (23); D.39 (15½).

The crest 'a sun, or, between two branches in orle' belongs

100

100

to the Jacksons of Kelwoolds Grove, Yorkshire, accordingly the ivory monogram must stand for W. S. Jackson, but the motto is fictitious.

The chair closely follows a popular design in A. W. N. Pugin's *Gothic Furniture in the Style of the Fifteenth Century*, 1835, pl.5. A pair of chairs in the chancel of Ilkley church correspond to this engraving.

LIT: D. Linstrum, 'Pugin Furniture at Lotherton', *L.A.C.*, No.70 (1972), pp.26–29, fig.1.

PROV: By descent through the Jackson family of Leeds; the original owner may have been William Scarborough Jackson, tobacco manufacturer, who in 1866 lived in Headingley, Leeds; bequeathed by Wilfred Jackson 1947.

[25.1/47]

101

101 ARMCHAIR
Possibly by Jackson and Graham, London
c.1878
Ebonized mahogany; pine

Of rectangular design with a deep sprung seat and solid upholstered back headed by a spindle gallery and top-rail incised with a gilt demi-lunette pattern centering on a rayed medallion; the block turned uprights and rails are enriched

101

102 SET OF TEN DINING CHAIRS
Possibly by Edwards and Roberts, London
*c.*1880
Mahogany; beech

The open vase-shaped splats enriched with rococo foliage and gothic details in the Chippendale taste support shaped crestings outlined with leafy scrolls centering on a chinoiserie bell, fluted back posts; square front legs braced by fretted spandrels and styled on two faces with gothic tracery headed by bells, the splayed rear legs are similarly carved on one flank; sprung red leather seats, the beech rails faced with a decorative mahogany bead; formerly fitted with castors.
H.97 (38½); W.59 (23); D.48 (19).

A similar dining chair in the V. & A. (W.6–1945) bears a fragmentary trade label of Edwards and Roberts, the high class London furnishers. It is significant that a card table (Cat. No.555) at Lotherton, also from Wentbridge House, was supplied by the same firm.

PROV: Acquired at the time of his marriage in 1883 by Edmund Leatham, Wentbridge House, Yorkshire; inherited by Lady Gascoigne; the Gascoigne gift 1970.   [38/70]

with gilt rings and incised lines, while the padded arms rest on rows of turned spindles; the back posts support ball finials and the legs, united by rods, formerly had socket castors. The stuffed-over seat, buttoned back and arms were originally covered in green velvet.
H.91 (36); W.61 (24); D.61 (24).

The chair is virtually identical to a woodcut in C. L. Eastlake's *Hints on Household Taste*, 4th ed., 1878, p.165. According to the text the illustration represents a 'drawing-room chair manufactured by Messrs Jackson and Graham' which demonstrates 'how easily a few incised patterns and turned mouldings may be substituted for the lumpy carving and "shaped" legs usually found in such furniture'. There is no evidence that Eastlake contributed this design, he apparently featured it as a good example of high quality progressive commercial furniture. Because *Hints on Household Taste* was so influential there is no way of knowing if this particular chair was produced by Jackson and Graham or copied from the book plate by another firm.

PROV: J. A. West (Antiques), Whitehaven; W. Waters; bought from the Lotherton Endowment Fund 1975.
[6/75]

102

103 CHILD'S ARMCHAIR ON STAND

*c.*1885

Mahogany; beech

The chair is secured to a low stand by a thumb-screw which passes through the medial stretcher and the platform base, allowing it to be used independently of the lower stage. The stand has a rectangular top, straight legs braced by H-pattern stretchers and simple corner mouldings; the chair is styled in the Hepplewhite taste with a curved, lightly channelled top rail and back posts enclosing a pierced, vase-shaped splat, the straight front legs are drilled with peg-holes to support an adjustable footboard and the arm terminals are bored to received a bar with turned end knobs one of which unscrews. Upholstered in green plush with a double row of brass nails, beech seats rails.

H.89 (35); chair unit 56 (22); W.39 (15½); D.33 (13).

PROV: Acquired for Lorna, daughter of Edmund Leatham, Wentbridge House, Yorkshire; the Gascoigne gift 1968.

[7.189/68]

104 ARMCHAIR

By Collinson & Lock, London

*c.*1886

Rosewood; beech, ivory

The rectangular, slightly curved back, centres on a square padded panel framed between narrow uprights with a spindle gallery below and a row of Ionic scrolls above; the shaped crest rail, set between crozier backposts, is inlaid with a vase of fruit and elaborately scrolled foliage incorporating dolphins' heads executed in engraved ivory. The slender arms rest on turned vase-pattern supports; square tapered front legs, the beech seat rails faced with rosewood veneer. The principal members are outlined with ivory strings. Originally covered in a gold silk fabric.

H.96 (38); W.54 (21¼); D.51 (20).

This chair was illustrated in the *Cabinet Maker & Art Furnisher*, 1 Dec. 1886, pp.143–4 as the work of Messrs. Collinson & Lock, Oxford Street, London, being described as '. . . rosewood, richly inlaid with engraved ivory, in the Renaissance style.'

PROV: Lord Airedale; given by the Misses Hawkyard 1968.

[15.3/68]

103

104

105 PAIR OF CHAIRS
Made by Brew & Co, London
1886
Rosewood; beech, ivory

The backs centre on a padded shield-shaped panel set in a rectangular frame headed by a serpentine cresting and joined to the slender crozier back post by a bridge carved with husks; the sprung, stuffed-over seats are raised on straight tapered forelegs with spade feet and curving rear supports; the back of each is inlaid with classical foliage and husks executed in engraved ivory and outlined with strings; the veneered beech seat rails and legs are also panelled with ivory strings headed by floral medallions.
H.86 (33¾); W.40 (16); D.39 (15½).

The original suite consisted of a settee, two arm and six single chairs upholstered in a golden brown Genoa cut-velvet.
A label sewn to the underside of one chair (and three others in the suite) is printed 'BREW & COMPY (the name CLARIS cancelled) / CABINET MAKERS / & UPHOLS-TERERS / 54, FINSBURY PAVEMENT EC / WHOLE-SALE AND EXPORT' and in ink 'Nov. 23rd 1886 / The suite of furniture made of Rosewood, inlaid with engraved ivory, of which this piece forms a part, was manufactured by us for the Boudoir and Drawing Room of H.R.H. the Princess of Wales in the Colonial and Indian Exhibition, South

Kensington, 1886. Brew & Coy.' *The Cabinet-Maker & Art Furnisher*, 1886, pp.309–11 contains a description of rooms provided for the accommodation of royalty at the above exhibition and illustrates a 'Queen Anne' corner and a 'Jacobean' corner furnished by Brew & Co.

LIT: G. Wills, *English Furniture 1760–1900*, 1971, p.249, pl.199.

PROV: Made for the drawing room and boudoir of H.R.H. the Princess of Wales at the Colonial and Indian Exhibition, South Kensington in 1886; Louis Learmouth; auctioned by Phillips, Son & Neale, 9 Dec. 1930, lot 41; given by Mrs Ivy Learmouth 1970.　　[9/70]

106 CHAIR
Late 19th century
Walnut; beech, oak, mahogany

The rectangular upholstered back and stuffed-over seat are supported on four cabriole legs carved at the knee with a lion's-mask and ribbon motif suspending a leaf-pendant, terminating in lion's-paw and ball feet. Upholstered in early Georgian *gros-point* needlework the cover slightly extended at the edges and secured by brass nails. Walnut, with oak side, beech back and mahogany front rails.
H.99 (39); W.59 (23); D.53 (21).

105

106

The needlework matches the panels mounted on one of another pair of lion's-mask chairs (Cat. No.107). The group can be identified with an entry in the 1930s Lotherton inventory '3 Ball and Claw Gros Point Worked Chairs – came from Parlington; one found in Saddle room in shocking condition.' Apparently a Victorian reproduction mounted with old needlework.

PROV: The Gascoignes of Parlington Hall; removed to Lotherton Hall; the Gascoigne gift 1968. [7.180/68]

107 PAIR OF CHAIRS
Late 19th century
Mahogany and beech

En suite, apart from minor carved details, with Cat. No.106 but with the feet hollowed for brass castors stamped 'COPE'. The early Georgian needlework on one chair matches the cover on Cat. No.106, the other is worked in the same colours but with a larger floral design; each frame has an original beech back rail uniting genuine demi lion's-mask rear legs in mahogany; the forelegs carved in beech treated with mahogany stain might be old, originally gesso-gilt members, but are probably late Victorian copies.
H.99 (39); W.61 (24); D.53 (21).

The Lotherton collection contained many reproduction items including a Queen Anne style needlework chair by Lenygon and a large square stool by Joubert with lion's-mask legs corresponding to the front members on this pair of chairs, which are interesting hybrid examples of Victorian taste. The Parlington sale (1905) included nine pieces of lion's-mask seat furniture, lots 90–4 of the same dubious character.

PROV: See previous entry. [7.174/68]

108 SET OF EIGHT CHAIRS
*c.*1894 (one *c.*1700)
Walnut

High backs with turned uprights, the splats and crestings elaborately carved and pierced in the style of about 1700; turned and faceted legs united by shaped cross-stretchers centering on a finial; the seats upholstered in orange uncut moquette.
H.130 (51½); W.52 (20½); D.44 (17½).

Only one chair is late Stuart in date the other seven being copies. The original model, which has itself been extensively restored, is distinguished by copious worm holes, beech seat rails and comparatively shallow carving; the copies have oak rails and display a higher technical finish (the perplexing inscription 'WK/1747' is scratched behind the cresting of one).

The chairs were very probably bought by Mrs E. C. Meynell Ingram as a supporting cast for the great neo-Elizabethan staircase built at Temple Newsam under the direction of C. E. Kempe in 1894, since four of them are visible in a photograph of the upper stairway published in *Country Life*, 8 Oct. 1904, p.525.

LIT: *Apollo*, Dec. 1941, p.139, fig. iv.

EXH: *Temple Newsam Heirlooms*, 1972 (38).

WK 1747

PROV: The Hon. Mrs E. C. Meynell Ingram, Temple Newsam; given by the Earl of Halifax 1922.   [1922/F9]

109 SET OF FOUR SINGLE AND TWO ARMCHAIRS
19th century, last quarter
Oak; beech

The armchairs have turned uprights, elaborately carved and
pierced backs in the late Stuart style, scrolled arms and bun
feet united by cross-stretchers; the seats are stuffed with hair
and covered in blue and white machine-woven floral tapestry. The single chairs have spiral twist back posts, padded
backs framed by elaborately carved borders and turned
stretchers, the upholstery matches that on the armchairs.
Armchairs: H.129 (51); W.61 (24); D.53 (21).
Single: H.125 (49); W.48 (19); D.46 (18).

Illustrations of the Great Hall at Temple Newsam published in *Magazine of Art*, 1893, p.210 and by F. Moss,

Pilgrimages to Old Homes, V, 1910, p.319 show the room heavily
furnished with Victorian chairs from this suite intended to
harmonize with the picturesque neo-Elizabethan decor.

PROV: See previous entry.   [1922/F.21]

110 SET OF FOUR CHAIRS
c.1900
Mahogany

The reeded back posts support a plain top rail with twin
reeded crossbars connected by billets and a bottom rail
carved with eight swags of drapery; the slip seats are raised
on straight channelled forelegs; side, medial and rear stretchers. The seat bases and rails are incised 'I, II, VI, VIII'.
H.84 (33); W.49 (19½); D.40 (16).

PROV: Agnes and Norman Lupton Bequest 1953. [13.391/53]

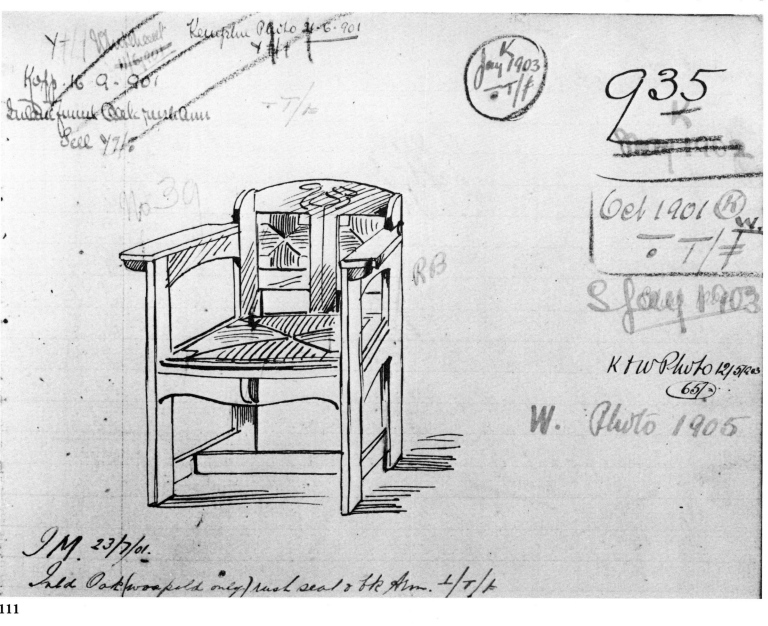

111 ARMCHAIR
By William Birch & Co, High Wycombe, probably to a design by E. G. Punnett
*c.*1901
Fumed oak; walnut, ebony

The low back, framing twin rush panels divided by a central splat, supports a curved cresting inset with a walnut tablet enclosing an art nouveau stem motif executed in ebony; the uprights, flat arms resting on arched bridge rails, shaped seat frame and plain stretchers are constructed of broad $\frac{3}{4}$ inch staves united by dowel tenons; the rush slip seat drops in to a slightly splayed frame with a rounded front supported on a corbel. One seat rail is inscribed $\frac{3C}{957}$ in pencil.

H.85 (33$\frac{3}{4}$); W.54 (21$\frac{1}{2}$); D.48 (19$\frac{1}{2}$).

The manuscript design together with a cost analysis of this chair survives amongst the Birch papers at High Wycombe Library and Museum. The sketch sheet is numbered 935 and annotated with various names, dates and codes ranging between June 1901 and 1905. An inscription in the top left-hand corner reads 'Kopp 16.9.901 / inlaid fumed oak rush arm / Sell Y7/6' (which translates at 72/6d.). A later October 1901 reference gives 65/- and this price is confirmed by another note 'K & W Photo 12/5/903 65/-'. The following legend occurs below the design 'J.M 23/7/01, Inld Oak, (wax pold only) rush seat & bk Arm'.
The cost schedule headed '935 Inld Oak rush seat & back arm Pol 1179 30.5.1' records:

Wood	9.0
Making frame	18.0
Machining	2.0
Inlaying	1.0
Marqueterie	1.6
Polishing	3.6
Material	6
Saw Mach	1.0
Rushing	2.6
Rushes	1.0
Incidentals	6.0
	————
	2.6.0

According to Elizabeth Aslin, who in 1959 interviewed William Birch (aged over eighty) grandson of the founder, this chair was designed by E. G. Punnett who moved from J. S. Henry to Birch & Co in 1901. The firm apparently made furniture to Punnett's design for Liberty's and it is interesting that his name occurs on a dozen or so sketch sheets, all dated between March and November 1901. The attribution to Punnett is reasonably sound but not proven. There is an unexplained discrepancy in the code 3C/957 pencilled on the seat rail of this example and the firm's pattern books which illustrates a Sheraton style chair under that number. Several identical chairs exist, the best known being at the V. & A. (CIRC. 400–1959).

PROV: Said to come from a Welsh collection; W. Waters;
bought from the Lotherton Endowment Fund 1975.

[22/75]

112 PAIR OF CHAIRS
Probably by Heal & Sons, London
*c.*1903
Mahogany; beech, box

The shield-shaped backs have pierced vase-pattern splats centering on oval fan medallions; the square tapered forelegs ending in spade feet, front rail and back frame are inlaid with boxwood strings; rounded rear legs, twin side stretchers of turned beech finished in mahogany stain; cane seat.
H.86 (34); W.42 (16$\frac{1}{2}$); D.38 (15).

Formerly one of three, probably supplied by Heal & Son with other bedroom furniture (Cat. No.8) in 1903. Almost exactly similar chairs appear in the firm's trade catalogues illustrating 'Sheraton' bedroom suites.

PROV: Lotherton Hall; the Gascoigne gift 1971.   [23.24/71]

112

113 PAIR OF ARMCHAIRS

Early 20th century
Birch, mahogany

The heart-shaped backs are formed of three interlacing lobes festooned with drapery, the upper loops enclosing Prince of Wales feathers and knotted ribbons; curved arms on swept supports enriched with husks; serpentine-fronted compass seats covered in modern fabric raised on tapering panelled legs headed by blocks set with paterae and fluted cappings above. The birch rear legs are heavily stained and the mahogany front legs and arms painted to simulate satinwood. H.95 (37½); W.59 (23); D.52 (20½).

The diversity of grained and stained timber combined with the 'Edwardian' elaboration of the splat and leg headings indicate the chairs are reproductions which have received cosmetic treatment to make them appear old.

LIT: *L.A.C.*, No.60 (1967), p.9, fig.2; C. G. Gilbert, *L.G. & R.F.*, 1972, p.31, repr.

PROV: Bequeathed by Frank Savery 1966.·   [1.7/66]

114 ARMCHAIR

By Edwin Nichols, Ltd, Worcester
c.1905
Mahogany; satinwood, beech

The back is composed of moulded members forming an interlaced heart design incorporating Prince of Wales feathers and festooned drapery in satinwood; the curved arms and swept supports enriched with satinwood elbow rosettes and husk drops rest on fluted blocks; straight, tapered forelegs panelled on two sides and headed by paterae, curved back legs with pointed toes; the serpentine-fronted seat is covered in modern fabric stuffed over beech rails. H.90 (35½); W.61 (24); D.51 (20).

Formerly one of a pair, this chair bears a circular printed label on the back rail 'ESTABLISHED 1880 / EDWIN NICHOLS Ltd, / House Furnishers / and Cabinet Makers / New Street / WORCESTER'.

PROV: Sir Douglas Galton of Himbleton Manor, Worcs, bought several pieces of reproduction or heavily restored furniture from Nichols; some passed to his daughter Gwendolen Gascoigne, were taken to Lotherton and descended to her son Sir Alvary; the Gascoigne gift 1968.   [7.190/68]

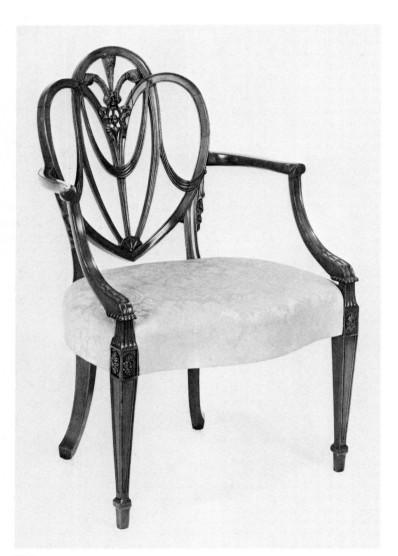

113   114

115 ARMCHAIR
By J. R. Teale & Son, Leeds
*c.*1905
Oak; beech

Carved, gondola back with central splat and hooped elbows; the serpentine-fronted seat is stuffed and covered in American cloth secured by brass studs, turned legs. Beech seat rails veneered with oak; castors removed and legs cut down by about an inch.
H.84 (33); W.51 (20); D.51 (20).

Labelled on seat rail 'J. R. TEALE & SON / CITY CABINET WORKS / 20, UPPERHEAD ROW / LEEDS / Workman's Name . . . . .'. There are six identical chairs by Teale & Son in Leeds Town Hall.

PROV: Temple Newsam; given by the Earl of Halifax 1922.
[1922/F52]

116 REVOLVING OFFICE CHAIR
*c.*1910
Walnut

The open gondola back has a pierced central splat designed in the Chippendale style and raked arm supports; the broad, deeply dished saddle seat is raised on a claw with four curved

legs ending in blind scroll toes and brown pottery castors. Cast-iron swivel plate.
H.86 (34); W.61 (24); D.53 (21).

Closely similar models are illustrated in furniture trade catalogues of Modern Office Chairs issued about 1910 by William Birch, High Wycombe (75.10/72) and Shannon, Ltd, London (226.10/72).

PROV: Lotherton Hall; the Gascoigne gift 1972.   [2/72]

CHANDELIERS
Electric Lights

117 CHANDELIER
By John Giles, London
1738
Brass

Quadruple baluster stem of vase design supporting twenty-four S-scrolled branches arranged in two tiers terminating in nozzles and circular grease pans; inscribed round the base 'EDM: SMITH SURGEON GAVE THIS TO YE CHURCH OF CHELTENHAM ANO: DOM: 1738'.
H.127 (50).

John Giles, brassfounder, can be identified as the author of this chandelier on the evidence of stylistic analogy with a documented pair which he supplied to St Dionis, Backchurch, London in 1740 and one in the church at Framlingham, Suffolk signed and dated 'JOHN GILES FECIT 1742'. Eleven of the cast patterns are also repeated on an undated pair hanging at Rotherhithe, indicating that all six were produced in the same foundry.

The Cheltenham chandelier is of special technical and art-historical importance as a new design type, being the earliest recorded example in which the branches are bolted onto collars surrounding the globes instead of being hooked onto the stem above a single orb. The holes for the reception of the branches are lettered A–Z to ensure correct assembly. The shaft elements are core cast.

A number of alterations were made when the chandelier was converted to use with gas sometime after 1866. In order to create a continuous system of tubing the suspension ring and nozzles, being solid, were removed, the two plain lengths of curve on each branch cut away and the elaborately styled parts drilled before being re-soldered on to new sections of piping, thus apart from the addition of taps, the appearance of the branches was scarcely affected; internally the central iron rod was removed and radial tubing installed. During the present century the chandelier was wired for electricity, but is now restored almost to its intact state. However, the original gilt-metal hanging rods, the suspension and terminal rings (of scrolled design matching those at St Dionis and Framlingham) have not survived.

117

LIT: R. Sherlock, 'A Chandelier for Temple Newsam', *L.A.C*, No.57 (1965), pp.14–23, repr.; R. Sherlock, 'The Cheltenham Chandelier', *Connoisseur*, Feb. 1965, pp.81–5, repr.; R. Sherlock, 'Chandeliers in Gloucestershire Churches', *Transactions of the Bristol and Gloucestershire Archaeological Society*, 1965, pp.111–12, repr.; *Burlington*, May 1965, p.282, fig.91; R. Gentle, *English Domestic Brass*, 1975, fig.119.

PROV: Given to St Mary's Parish Church, Cheltenham by Edmund Smith in 1738 where it hung in the nave until 1838 and was sold by the church wardens following the vestry meeting on 26 April 1855; acquired by John E. W. Rolls for his large country house The Hendre, nr. Monmouth and shown amongst period furnishing in the Great Hall in a photograph of 1865; by descent through the Lords Llangattock to Colonel J. C. E. Harding Rolls; Christie's, 28 Nov. 1963, lot 15; Pratt & Burgess, Ltd; bought with the aid of a government grant 1964.   [10/64]

118 CHANDELIER
*c.*1755
Gilt pine

The elaborately flared and pierced lower member is carved with rococo swirls, cabochon motifs, fronds and tooled flame ornament with a tiered palm-leaf formation above; the

stem supports eight double-scrolled branches with foliate terminals and turned candleholders; the arms and sockets are incised with Roman numerals. An iron rod passes through the hollow body ending in a buckle-shaped pendant. Wired for electricity.
H.77 (30½); Diam. 96 (38).

EXH: Temple Newsam, *Thomas Chippendale*, 1951 (129).

PROV: Alfred Jowett; Charles Lumb & Sons; bought 1950.
                                                    [38/50]

119 CHANDELIER
Late 18th century
Cut glass

The bowl is fitted with a silvered liner and brass receiver plate into which the twenty-four notched S-pattern arms, arranged in two tiers, are socketed; the arms terminate in modern star-shaped drip-pans and candleholders. The stem centres on a fluted classical vase set between baluster components with an elaborate base element ending in a richly faceted cone. The corona is festooned with prismatic bead-chains connected to the arms which are themselves linked by and suspend further cut glass drops ending in faceted pear-shaped pendants. Wired for electricity.
H.122 (48).

PROV: The Earls of Halifax, Hickleton Hall, Yorkshire; Hickleton Hall sale (Hollis & Webb, Leeds) 18–22 March 1947, lot 22; Thornton (Antiques) York; bequeathed by Sir George Martin 1976.   [51.14/76]

120 CHANDELIER
Early 19th century
Cut glass

The central notched stem ornamented with a wrythen knop is crowned by a slice-cut corona fringed with cut bead-drops and carries a smaller medial corona; the fourteen cable-twisted branches of S-scroll design supporting rosette drip-pans and lights arranged in two tiers, radiate from a broad shallow star-cut dish ringed with a diamond pattern band; the stem terminates in a small chain-hung finial and a large faceted drop; the arms are profusely festooned with wired bead-chains and cut pendants; the silvered metal suspension rod is mounted with a socketed wheel into which the branches, masked by the dished base, are set.
H.117 (48).

Typical of the chandeliers made by Perry during the late Georgian period. The receiver bowl covering the arm plate is almost certainly a replacement; it appears to be a flat dish light of Regency date.

PROV: The Earls of Halifax; bought at the Hickleton Hall sale (Hollis & Webb, Leeds) 18–22 March 1947, lot 119.
                                                    [12.1/47]

118

121 CHANDELIER
By F. & C. Osler, Birmingham
19th century, second half
Cut glass

The trumpet-shaped finial and six scrolled arms hung with lustres rise from a small cup with a heavily fluted baluster stem and ball section below; a medial cup supports six tall barley-twist scrolls crowned by 'icicle' spires and the twelve curving candle-branches arranged in two tiers spring from a large solid bowl element ending in a richly faceted pendant; the arms and drip-pans are lavishly festooned with cut bead-chains, prismatic drops and globe pendants; the silvered central stem supports three radial components with numbered dovetail sockets into which the arms slot and the shaft is impressed 'F & C OSLER'.
H.137 (54).

F. & C. Osler of Birmingham were important Victorian glass merchants specializing in large scale ornamental products. Typical of chandeliers made by Osler in the second half of the century and mainly in original condition although the visible shaft top indicates a short section of the stem is missing.

LIT: *L.A.C.*, No.6 (1948), p.6, repr.

PROV: Charles Thornton (Antiques) York; given by F. E. Tetley 1948. [36/48]

CHANDELIER, brass
Supplied by G. F. Bodley, 1877
Under Cat. No.529

121

122 CHANDELIER

Probably by Thomas Elsley, London
1894
Brass

The central baluster and vase-turned shaft with a globular base supports two tiers of six elaborately scrolled S-shaped branches ending in plain drip-pans and nozzles; the arms are fastened by screws to ring collars.
H.64 (25).

Ordered for the staircase at Temple Newsam. On 6 July 1894 Freddie Wood informed Mrs Meynell Ingram 'I have written about a chain for the staircase spider . . .'. Further details under Cat. No.123.

LIT: F. Moss, *Pilgrimages to Old Homes*, V, 1910, p.303, repr.
[1922/F44]

123 CHANDELIER

Probably by Thomas Elsley, London
1894
Brass
Of similar design to Cat. No.122 but with three tiers of six lights each and a larger terminal globe.

This chandelier was hung originally in the dining room at Temple Newsam but has since been suspended in the main stairwell for which the companion chandelier was provided. Both were supplied in 1894 for the interiors decorated in Jacobean style by Messrs. Norman & Burt of Burgess Hill, Sussex to the designs of C. E. Kempe. The chandeliers were probably acquired from Thomas Elsley of London who can be associated with the built-in sideboard (Cat. No.343) and brass andirons in the dining room; he regularly supplied Norman & Burt with ornamental metalwork for schemes devised by C. E. Kempe.
H.96 (38).

LIT: C. G. Gilbert, 'C. E. Kempe's Staircase and Interiors at Temple Newsam 1894', *L.A.C.*, No.65 (1969) pp.6–11.

PROV: The Hon. Mrs E. C. Meynell Ingram of Temple Newsam; given by the Earl of Halifax 1922   [1922/F45]

124 CHANDELIER

Late 19th century
Glass and ormolu

The ormolu panache finial and corona, styled in the rococo taste, are hung with a flared screen of graduated bead-chains secured to an ornate medial hoop supporting four sets of triple candle branches richly chased with rococo foliage and scrolls; the lower festoons converge on an ormolu grape finial to form a hemi-spherical base curtain; tubular rods radiate from the central globe to each set of lights; wired for electricity.
H.89 (35).

PROV: The first Harrogate Antique Dealers' Fair, 1951; Philip Rakusen; given by Alderman and Mrs S. Symmonds 1969.   [17/69]

125 TABLE LIGHT

By Thomas Elsley to the design of C. F. A. Voysey
*c.*1898
Bronze

The circular block base with a dished top supports a slender column headed by a tulip-shaped bulb holder; the base incorporates a switch-lever with a heart-shaped leaf terminal. Original flex sheathed in green silk and turned wooden plug. Electrical components stamped 'REGD 292069'. The shade is missing.
H.33 (13).

125

125

One of six formerly at Moor Crag: two are now at Brighton Art Gallery and one was acquired by Abbot Hall Art Gallery, Kendal. They have 'mushroom' shades of green pleated silk which could be original, but other lamps designed by Voysey had copper reflectors over the horns. A table light of identical design is illustrated in an undated catalogue in the R.I.B.A. Drawings Collection (Voysey, Box XI) titled *Thomas Elsley Ltd, 28 and 30 Grt Titchfield Street, Designs by C. F. Voysey, Architect*, p.7, No.Z11E (price £2.15.0).

PROV: Ordered by J. W. Buckley, Moor Crag, Windermere; his daughter Mrs H. I. L. Speller; bequeathed to Miss D. M. Dixon; bought from the Lotherton Endowment Fund 1976. [23.2/76]

126 PAIR OF ELECTRIC PENDANTS
By Thomas Elsley to the design of C. F. A. Voysey
c.1898
Bronze; clouded glass

The circular concave-sided shades are encircled by a suspension clip-collar designed as a coronet with four scrolled canopy ribs ending in leafy finials.
H.23 (9); Diam. 15 (6).

Two of many uniform light fittings installed at Moor Crag.

126

A shade holder of identical design is illustrated in an undated catalogue in the R.I.B.A. Drawings Collection (Voysey, Box X1) titled *Thomas Elsley Ltd, 28 and 30 Grt Titchfield Street, Designs by C. F. Voysey, Architect*, p.10, No.75E (price 17/6).

PROV: Ordered by J. W. Buckley, Moor Crag, Windermere; his daughter Mrs H. I. L. Speller; bequeathed to Mrs D. M. Dixon; bought from the Lotherton Endowment Fund 1976. [23.3/76]

ELECTRIC LIGHT FITTINGS AT LOTHERTON

Lotherton Hall was greatly enlarged and modernized during the early Edwardian period; a private generator was installed about 1900–2 and the phased architectural improvements that followed serve to date the electric fittings in different parts of the house. In 1903 the large drawing room and vestibule with bedrooms over were built and the hall and staircase remodelled. The majority certainly and perhaps all the light fittings for these interiors were supplied by Perry & Co. Ltd, 17 Grafton Street, London. The library, dining and morning rooms were redesigned in 1907–8, each being equipped with a chandelier and wall brackets wired for electricity. Lady Sandys, who was brought up at Lotherton during this period, recalls that the lights in the boudoir and morning room were bought in Paris. The two fittings (Cat. Nos.138 & 139) bearing design registration numbers confirm the dates based on architectural evidence. One chandelier by Perry (Cat. No.131) was sold to Leeds for display at Temple Newsam in 1955 and has since been returned to its original setting. One suite of sconces (Cat. No.142) came from the Gascoignes' London house.

127 SHADE LIGHT

*c.*1900
Brass and glass

The half-round bowl is formed as a screen of faceted and graduated beads strung from an ormolu corona to a small prism element in the base; the hoop is enriched with acanthus and suspended from three square-link chains.
H.23 (9); Diam.33 (13).

Installed in one of the Lotherton bedrooms.

PROV: The Gascoigne gift 1968. [7.654/68]

128 DISH LIGHT

*c.*1900
Brass and glass

The circular shade is designed as a shallow bowl of frosted glass engraved with six blossoms and mounted in an enriched brass corona; the three suspension chains incorporate fruit-pattern links.
Diam. 35 (14).

Installed in one of the Lotherton bedrooms.

PROV: The Gascoigne gift 1968. [7.653/68]

129 PAIR OF WALL LIGHTS (French)

*c.*1900
Glass and brass

The mural tablets, profiled as baroque vases with fronded terminals and shoulders, each support three arms of broken-scroll design ending in rosette pattern pans fitted with mock-candle bulb holders, the finials are formed of a moulded glass bottle; the arms and minor wire brackets set with moulded florets and large prismatic drops. Each plate is stamped behind '200'.
H.40 (16).

Installed in the boudoir at Lotherton.

PROV: The Gascoigne gift 1968. [7.649/68]

130 CHANDELIER (French)
*c.*1900
Glass and brass

The central shaft is composed of four rods enclosed by three brass ribs of broken-scroll design forming a vase-shaped cage; the upper plate supports three curved brackets and three arms, terminating in rosette pattern pans fitted with mock-candle bulb sockets, spring from the lower plate; the skeleton bears numerous spurs hung with large globular or pear-shaped pendants, faceted drops and small moulded florets. H.61 (24).

Installed in the boudoir at Lotherton.

PROV: The Gascoigne gift 1968.   [7.648/68]

131 CHANDELIER
By Perry & Co, London
*c.*1903
Glass and brass

The closely festooned graduated drops cascade and spread from a small corona to a large metal hoop ornamented with Vitruvian scrolls and hung with faceted bead chains forming a hemi-spherical curtain; the central rod, crowned by a fronded gilt-metal panache finial above the dome canopy, terminates in a ball pendant and is tied to the medial hoop by braces alternating with nine leafy scrolling branches arranged in two tiers, the glass light shades enriched with nail patterns; the tubular frame is wired for electricity. H.183 (72).

An inventory of Lotherton Hall compiled in the 1930s records '1 Cut Glass Chandelier – Copy of old. Made by Perry', the entry undoubtedly relates to this example which was ordered for the drawing room built in 1903. Perry & Co (formerly in partnership with Parker) were old established makers of quality chandeliers; in 1900–1 they were trading as Electric Light Fitters at 17, Grafton Street, London.

PROV: Bought from Sir Alvary Gascoigne, Lotherton Hall
1955.   [26.48/55]

132 SET OF FOUR WALL LIGHTS
By Perry & Co, London
*c.*1903
Brass

The tapering fluted shafts decorated with husk chains are headed by blocks supporting tied ribbons and terminate below in fruit pendants; each sconce has three curved reeded branches styled with leaf sheaths and bearing ornamental nozzles; wired for electricity and fitted with hollow glass candles concealing stem sockets engaged to box wood insulators. Numbered components, the back of each impressed 'PERRY'.

131

H.60 (23½).

Ordered together with the chandelier (Cat. No.131) for the drawing room at Lotherton, built in 1903.

PROV: The Gascoigne gift 1968.   [7.644/68]

132

133 PAIR OF WALL LIGHTS
Probably by Perry & Co, London
*c.*1903
Glass and brass

The brass back plates of oval fan-patera design each support a short arm terminating in a circular element set with two reeded brass arms, a tall glass spire and two ornamented brackets hung with drops; the bell finial, base pendant and cut glass nozzles are festooned with faceted bead chain and prismatic drops; wired for electricity and fitted with mock-candle bulb sockets.
H.51 (20).

The department of Prints & Drawings at the V. & A. contains two sketch books by John Wateridge (95 C.83) who worked for Perry & Co as a designer until 1925 when the firm was taken over by Burt Escare. Several of his drawings are similar to these wall lights.
Installed in the boudoir at Lotherton.

PROV: The Gascoigne gift 1968.   [7.646/68]

133

134

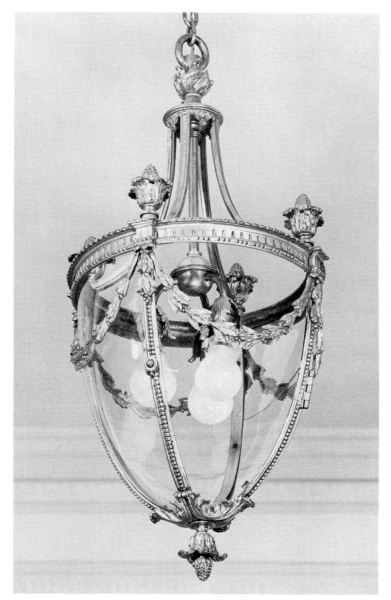

135

134 LANTERN
Probably by Perry & Co, London
c.1903
Brass and glass

The ovoid shade, formed of six frosted panes framed by brass straps ornamented with husk chains, tapers to an elaborately fronded rosette fruit pendant; one segment is hinged at the top giving access to four bulbs socketed into a central ball; the corona ring, banded with acanthus, is tied to a leaf-cup suspension fitment by a rib canopy decorated with shields, each stamped '8201'.
H.96 (38).

Installed in the entrance hall at Lotherton

PROV: The Gascoigne gift 1968.   [7.645/68]

135 LANTERN
By Perry & Co, London
c.1903
Brass and glass

Of vase design styled in the Adam manner; the gadrooned corona, with laurel swags below and four pineapple finials above, is tied to the fruit pendant by beaded ribs framing four clear glass panels, one segment being hinged as a door; the open canopy supports a flame finial and a suspension ring connected by a rod to the central globe fitted with three fronded bulb sockets; wired for electricity. The canopy is impressed 'PERRY 9015'.
H.81 (32); Diam. 35 (14).

Originally in the staircase well at Lotherton.

PROV: The Gascoigne gift 1968.   [7.643/68]

136 PAIR OF TWO-LIGHT SLIDING PENDANTS

*c.*1903
Brass and glass

The serpentine yokes, formed of hollow polished brass rods, terminate in pairs of cut glass drop shades; each bar centres on a globe with a pendant ring below and a spired column above braced by wrought C-scrolls; the fitment is suspended by electric flex from a system of pulleys incorporating ceramic wheels and a spherical counterweight encased in brass enabling the light to be adjusted for height.
W.66 (26).

Installed in a bedroom directly over the drawing room extension built in 1903; a third sliding pendant of identical design fitted with open flared shades survives.

PROV: The Gascoigne gift 1968.   [7.655/68]

137 PAIR OF WALL LIGHTS

*c.*1903
Brass

The canted stems are composed of a bulbous central section with a decorative vase above and an acorn pendant below in the Flemish taste; each supports three branches of broken-scroll design ending in square chamfered nozzles fitted with turned boxwood insulators and imitation candles; wired for electricity.
H.40 (16).

Installed in the entrance hall at Lotherton.

PROV: The Gascoigne gift 1968.   [7.652/68]

138 PAIR OF DROP LIGHTS

By Best and Rloyd Ltd, Birmingham
*c.*1903
Brass and glass

Each glass vase, etched with tied ribbons and paterae linked by garlands, is set in a brass corona decorated with floral swags; the bulb sockets are supported by husk-chains and the shades terminate below in an ornamental rosette and fruit pendant. Impressed (three times) '407773'.
H.28 (11).

The patent design No.407773 relates to a lamp shade registered by Best and Rloyd Ltd, Cambray Works, Hansworth, nr. Birmingham on 1st April 1903. The lights were installed in landing passages at Lotherton, there is a third damaged example in store.

PROV: The Gascoigne gift 1968.   [7.642/68]

139 CHANDELIER AND SET OF FOUR WALL LIGHTS

By Henry Bisseker, Birmingham
*c.*1908
Brass with an oxydized silver finish

The chandelier has a vase-shaped stem with a bulbous central section supporting six scrolled arms and terminates below in a mushroom pendant; the branches end in candle-holders fitted with bulb standards and clips stamped 'F & S 42'; defaced registration number on the suspension ring component; wired for electricity but adapted from a gasolier. The sconces have cartouche-shaped back plates with strap-work borders and a central shield headed by vase finials; a ball at the base of each supports two faceted and knopped branches of scroll design terminating in circular pans and candleholders; wired for electricity. The arms are impressed 'Rd 513770'.

138

Chandelier: H.106 (42).
Wall brackets: H.28 (11).

The design No. 513770 relates to a candle bracket registered by Henry Bisseker, 10–15 Bartholomew Street, Birmingham on 14 October 1907. According to the Birmingham directories Bisseker was a merchant, church bell and brass founder, weight and measure maker and an electric and gas fittings manufacturer.

Installed when the library at Lotherton was remodelled 1907–8.

PROV: The Gascoigne gift 1968.   [7.651/68]

139

140 CHANDELIER AND SET OF FOUR WALL LIGHTS
c.1908
Walnut and sycamore

The gilt sycamore chandelier has a turned shaft surmounted by a leaf-cup finial and terminates below in a flower-head pendant; the central knop supports five scrolled arms carved with fronds and ending in mock-candle sockets; the stem is pierced by a brass tube and the branches drilled for wiring. The lower section unscrews to disclose a cavity inscribed in pencil '807 5 Light'. The parcel-gilt walnut mural lights have split section brackets with pairs of arms corresponding to the stem and branches of the chandelier.
Chandelier: H.52 (20½).
Wall brackets: H.30.5 (12)

Installed when the dining room at Lotherton was remodelled 1907–8.

PROV: The Gascoigne gift 1968.   [7.650/68]

141 CHANDELIER AND SET OF FOUR WALL LIGHTS
c.1908
Gilt limewood

The chandelier has an elaborately carved upper shaft designed as an hexagonal vase and cover surmounted by a leaf-cup finial; the bulbous, heavily gadrooned base section terminating in a pineapple drop, supports six scrolled arms enriched with fronds ending in nozzles; the stem is pierced by a brass tube and the branches drilled for electric wiring, the lower stage unscrews. The wall brackets are of split-baluster design with a canted central section headed by a leafy vase-shaped finial and terminating below in a bulbous drop; the double C-scroll arms end in mock-candle sockets, decorated blue and gold. One pair has twin, the other single lights.
Chandelier: H.76 (30).
Wall bracket: H.40 (16)

Installed when the morning room at Lotherton was extended in 1908.

PROV: The Gascoigne gift 1968.   [7.647/68]

142 SET OF SIX WALL LIGHTS
c.1920
Copper and brass

Each back plate is profiled as a cartouche surmounted by a crown with a convex oval panel in the centre and two hollow brass arms ending in bulb sockets at the base; the set falls into three pairs of chinoiserie scenes depicted in gilt on a mottled red and black ground with matching borders and crowns, painted on die-stamped copper plates; wired for electricity.
H.38 (15).

PROV: Formerly at Heath Lodge, Hampstead; the Gascoigne gift 1971.   [23.12/71]

CHESTS

143 CHEST
Probably 16th century, second half
Oak

Of plank construction united by nails with the end members extended as legs divided by an inverted V-notch; the front is styled as four chip-carved panels bordered with cross-hatching; the middle pair display bifurcated arcades filled with lancet tracery while those at each side are ornamented with a leaf-pattern roundel and spandrels in the gothic taste framed by a simulated fielded panel; a subsidiary central panel beneath the lock plate bears crossed lancet leaves; the

143

interior formerly contained a lidded till on the left-hand side; the original staple hinges replaced by strap, H-pattern and now a fourth, modern set; fitted with an early but not the original lock and a later steel lock above, hasp fitment missing.

H.66 (26); W.136 (53½); D.49 (19½).

Several boarded chests of markedly similar character are recorded, but in the absence of dated examples it is not easy to place them. The simulated fielded panels might be interpreted as a late feature and the cross-hatching is odd, but the front displays few typical seventeenth century decorative elements and since it has not been carved-up in Victorian times the late sixteenth century seems plausible.

LIT: H. Cescinksy and E. Gribble, *Early English Furniture and Woodwork*, II, 1922, p.28, fig.30; *L.A.C.*, No.64 (1969), p.20, fig.1; *Connoisseur*, Aug. 1970, p.246, fig.6; G. Wills, *English Furniture 1550–1750*, 1971, p.21, pl.17.

PROV: W. Smedly Aston; the Gascoigne family, Lotherton Hall; the Gascoigne gift 1968. [7.139/68]

144 CHEST ON STAND
*c.*1600
Oak; lime

The lid is formed of three planks with bars at each end, two cross battens and a front rail banded with intarsia work; the walls are of plank construction with dovetailed corners and the base is adze finished underneath; the interior contains a lidded till on the left and a shallow trough on the right, both inlaid with geometric patterns; the ends, fitted with wrought-iron lifting handles fixed on foliated plates, are outlined with obliquely chequered panels; the front is sub-divided by applied strips inset with intarsia mosaics into two square and three upright panels faced with intarsia patterns, the narrow sections are decorated with geometric designs and the main panels each centre on a pair of tall spired and domed buildings with flag poles executed in light, dark and green-stained woods framed by chequered and interlaced bands between strings; the spectacular wrought-iron strap hinges secured by rivets and nails have elaborately scrolled and foliated terminals enhanced by engraving, the original tinned finish has been overpainted; within, the sides are reinforced by iron ties

144

and the corners with old hinge plates; original iron lock and key; the stand contains two drawers sliding on base runners, the lime drawer linings joined with dovetails and united to the bottom boards by wooden pegs; later brass handles and lock plate. Oak, with lime tills, drawer linings and riven corner blocks; the intarsia executed in ebonized and natural oak, light and stained woods. The geometric parquetry, running in discontinous patterns, suggests the intarsia facings were made in a specialist workshop.
H.94 (37); W.180 (71); D.69 (27).

The left-hand end panel is branded with a craftsman's mark 'I M'.

The boarded construction, dovetailed corners, pegged lime drawer linings, tinned hinges and use of intarsia as a decor-

ative technique are alien to the English craft tradition and indicate this chest was either made abroad or by a member of the immigrant colony of masters who worked in the Southwark district of London. Similar chests were made in Cologne during the late sixteenth century and the towered building is said to be a debased representation of Cologne Cathedral, depicted in greater detail on German chests of the same period. An article by Benno Forman 'Continental Furniture Craftsmen in London 1511–1625' in *Furniture History* VII (1971) discusses German prototypes and includes a list of furniture makers several of whom bear initials which correspond to the brand mark 'I M'.

This example is uncommonly large and unusual in that the narrow upright panels do not feature a stereotyped building; it is also rare to find chests with their original stand. The rather coarse technical finish and primitive pictorial panels suggest the chest was not imported from a continental style-centre but made by immigrants in England and probably post-dates the sophisticated example inscribed 1592 in the Lady Lever Art Gallery, Port Sunlight.

144

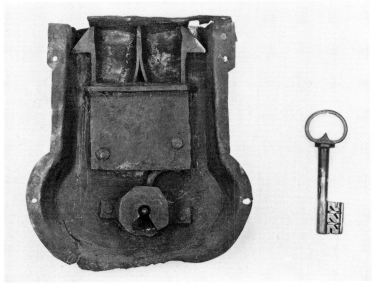

144

145 CHEST
17th century, second quarter
Oak

The front is divided into three arcaded panels embellished with shallow foliate carving and inlaid with a formal design of scrolled tendrils and conventional blossom in light and dark woods; the corner posts and stiles are decorated with flowering ferns and the rails inset with obliquely chequered bands, the upper rail being enhanced by a running pattern of fronded scrolls; plain side and back panels, moulded plank top, the hinges and lock plate renewed, hasp missing; the interior, which once contained a lidded till on the left-hand side is now fitted with a modern partition and base lining over the original bottom boards; pegged construction. Local restorations.
H.70 (27½); W.135 (53); D.56 (22).

The chequered bands, frieze decoration and upright fronds headed by flowers point to this chest being made in West Yorkshire, the inlay work suggests an urban centre.

LIT: G. Wills, *English Furniture 1550–1760*, 1971, p.18, pl.3 (colour).

144

145

PROV: Bequeathed by Mrs Emma Read, Leeds 1965.
[15.1/65]

146 CHEST
Mid 17th century
Oak

Of framed construction united by pegs with twin back and single side panels; nailed base boards and a moulded lid, supported on chamfered corner posts; the front is divided into three panels with sunk chip-carved decoration composed of four interlaced circles enclosing rosettes backed by fan fluting; the stiles are carved with a guilloche design between deeply gouged borders and the corner posts are incised with stiff ferns; the frieze is treated in an alternating pattern of fronded arcades and the bottom rail is channelled, both formations being repeated on the sides; the interior originally contained a till on the right; replaced strap hinges, lock missing, one rear leg restored.
H.75 (29½); W.137 (54); D.59 (23).

The character of the carving suggests a West Country origin.

PROV: The Wentworths of Bretton Hall, Wakefield, Yorkshire; given by Viscount Allendale 1947.   [4.3/47]

147 CHEST
17th century, second half
Oak

Of framed panel construction, the interior fitted with a small till on the right-hand side; richly carved front, the frieze rail combines a pattern of interlaced arcading with alternating stiff-leaf and floral motifs; the stiles and bottom rail are ornamented with circular interlace enclosing rosettes while the panels, of arcaded design with triangular frond spandrels and a lunette border, frame a simple floret; overall stamped enrichment. In recent times a hinged division has been made along the middle of the lid requiring the removal of two battens and reduction of the original wrought-iron hinge straps; internal lock missing.
H.70 (27½); W.140 (55); D.57 (22½).

It is noteworthy that a short section of inner border on the central panel is embellished with gadrooning whereas all the other surrounds carry a uniform lunette pattern; this sort of inconsistency in decorative idiom is not uncommon on seventeenth century furniture.

EXH: Leeds Art Gallery, *English Furniture*, 1930 (4).

PROV: Bequeathed by Mrs Frank Gott, Weetwood Garth, Leeds 1941.   [7.21/41]

146

148 CHEST

*c.*1685
Oak

Of framed construction with plain panelled ends and back and a moulded top bearing end battens, the bottom boards are supported by a medial brace and the interior originally contained an open till on the right-hand side. The top rail, decorated with serrated acanthus scrolls is incised 'RH/168', the bottom rail and stiles bear a simplified repeat of this foliate pattern while the corner posts are carved with undulating tulip trails; two central panels, each enriched with a formal design of scrolling stems, florets and tulips headed by oak leaves, are set between panels embellished with a similar composition of tulips and leaf blades; original wrought-iron strap hinges, hasp missing, lock plate renewed. The underside of the lid is lined with paper to stop dirt falling through the cracks.
H.74 (29); W.57 (145); D.61 (24).

The rugged carving, incomplete inscription and rough tool marks indicate a provincial origin. The undulating tulip band and botanical formulae are characteristic of West Yorkshire – there is a chest invested with markedly similar stylistic elements at Nostell Priory, near Wakefield (branded 'E.M.').

PROV: By descent in the Hopkinson family of Leeds to the donors Mrs A. Kenworthy, Mrs K. Taylor and Messrs E. & H. Pepper of Barnsley, Yorkshire; given 1974.
[4/74]

149 CHEST

*c.*1700
Oak

Of framed panel construction united by pegs with a plank lid and nailed base boards, the corner posts extended to form short legs; the front is divided into five panels carved with square rosettes, with three long fluted panels above; the rails and posts are channelled, the stiles edge-moulded, plain twin-panelled sides; the interior originally contained a till on the right-hand side, staple hinges replaced by iron straps, lock missing, some riven wood.
H.71 (28); W.162 (64); D.64 (25).

PROV: Given by Alderman Blanche Leigh 1938. [19/38]

147

148

CHESTS OF DRAWERS

150 CHEST OF DRAWERS
*c.*1655
Oak; fruitwood, lignum vitae, ivory

In two stages, the upper contains a shallow frieze drawer with a deep drawer below while the lower part has three drawers of equal depth enclosed by double doors; the front is

of architectural design being faced with bevelled panels framed by ripple and geometrically moulded borders divided by vase-shaped pilasters; the deep drawer, which centres on a perspective arch and the door panels are decorated with octagonal and rectangular parquetry patterns in ivory and ebonized wood; bricked cornice and corbelled frieze; the panelled back and sides incorporate riven and adzed timber.

The drawers, chamfered and nailed at the back with through dovetails at the front, slide on side runners, the lower tier pricked inside 'Top/M/B'; the frieze drawer can be locked by operating a swivel catch below the rail, the corbels and pilaster blocks serve as handle grips. Original wrought-iron ring-pulls survive on the lower drawers and rivet marks on the middle one indicate the position of a lock staple to secure

151

the doors; modern hinges and mortice locks. Oak carcase faced with panels of fruitwood, ivory and ebonized parquetry, lignum vitae ripple moulding. Minor restorations; no evidence for bun feet.

H.120 (47¼); W.110 (43½); D.65 (25½).

Early chests of drawers of this character often bear dates, generally ranging between *c.*1650 and 1665 inscribed on the inlaid ivory or pearl shell elements which help to date this example. The practice was evidently inspired by the tradition of carving dates on joined chests, but after the Restoration, cabinet makers rapidly abandoned this precedent favoured by their country cousins.

PROV: Acquired by the Hon. Marshall Brooks of Portal, Tarporley, Cheshire and sold by his grandson R. M. Brooks at Christie's, 25 April 1968, lot 103; bought 1968.

[9/68]

151 CHEST OF DRAWERS

*c.*1670
Cedar; fruitwood, oak, pine, beech, walnut

Built in two stages; the upper contains a shallow frieze drawer and a deep drawer below, the lower is fitted with two drawers of equal depth; they slide on side runners of beech and the fronts are divided into two bevelled, geometrically moulded panels with small applied ornaments; dentil cornice and corbelled-out frieze, the back and sides are of framed panel construction united by pegs, raised on short legs with modern bun feet; original wrought-iron drop-handles and lock plates. Cedar top and sides, the front faced with fruitwood and cedar mouldings, oak back, rails and corner posts, pine dustboards and bottom; oak drawer linings, the back boards with nailed and chamfered ends, crudely dovetailed at the front, the top is braced by a beech scantling with attached bark and an oak rail roughly carved with a fluted lunette pattern. Front base moulding renewed.
H.109 (43); W.104 (41); D.71 (28).

The back of the bottom drawer is indistinctively stamped 'WP' five times (presumably a craftsman's mark).

An interesting transitional piece: the chest is built in traditional joiners' fashion but was obviously intended to look like more sophisticated cabinet makers' furniture. The stamped initials, the use of random lengths of wood to underbrace the top, the glamorous timber and original mounts combine to make this chest of drawers an impressive document of the period.

PROV: A faded label pasted on top of the lower section is inscribed 'Mrs H. George'; bought from H. C. Foot (Antiques) 1941.   [26/41]

152 CHEST OF DRAWERS ON STAND

*c.*1680
Oak; walnut

In the form of a chest containing four long drawers mounted on a stand; the front is divided by moulded rails which extend as beaded partitions around the panelled sides; the corner posts and drawer centres are faced with small walnut panels bordered by oak mouldings and the double-fronted drawers are veneered in oak inset with a design of scrolling tendrils and stylized flowers in engraved bone and mother of pearl; the rectangular stand has five ring and knop turned supports connected by flat curved stretchers raised on bun feet; original cartouche pattern key escutcheons and rosette drop-handles cast in gilt brass. Of framed panel construction united by pegs with nailed bottom boards and some riven wood, the front is veneered with walnut and oak; crudely dovetailed drawers with chamfered backs sliding on side runners; six drawer runners renewed in beech, bun feet replaced, the stand reinforced with iron corner braces. Terminal wells in the corner posts indicate that the stand is rebuilt, evidence of colour and wear support this conclusion.
H.104 (41); W.101 (40); D.53 (21).

It is instructive to compare the crude enrichment with the sophisticated and technically much superior inlaid ornament executed in pearl shell and ivory on the oriental frame Cat. No.646. English craftsmen were attempting to imitate such exotic work imported by the East India Company.

LIT: *Antique Collector*, Feb. 1963, p.33, repr.

PROV: S. W. Wolsey (Antiques); bought with the aid of a government grant 1962.   [12.1/62]

153 CHEST OF DRAWERS ON STAND

*c.*1720
Walnut; pine, oak

The upper stage contains three short and three long drawers veneered in figured walnut outlined with feathered panels and cockbeaded; crossgrained cornice moulding and double half-round corner fillets; the top and sides laid with crossbanded veneers; mounted on a stand with shaped apron containing three drawers raised on four baluster turned legs with domed caps, and flat veneered cross-stretchers. Pine carcase and drawer linings, the bottom grain running from front to back. Brasses perhaps original.
H.157 (62); W.96 (38); D.60 (23½).

153

154

Heavily restored: apron and stretcher re-veneered, the feet and two baluster legs renewed in oak and the mushroom caps replaced, local reconditioning and repairs overall.

PROV: By descent to Mrs Frank Gott, Weetwood Garth who bequeathed it to Leeds 1941. [7.18/41]

154 CHEST OF DRAWERS
Late 18th century
Oak; mahogany, box

The top lifts up to reveal a well behind the upper row of dummy drawer fronts; below, a range of three short and two larger drawers with oak linings, the underside of each and corresponding opening incised with numerals: I–II–III–4–V; reeded corner pilasters above bracket feet. Oak carcase, panelled sides and back, the front veneered with mahogany and boxwood strings, the drawer fronts formed of oak panels with shaped mahogany surrounds. Brass handles and escutcheons not original.
H.97 (38½); W.155 (61); D.54 (21½).

A vernacular piece decorated in an elementary 'Sheraton' idiom often observed on rural corner cupboards and clockcases. This design type – a combination of a standard chest of drawers and a clothes chest – is found only in furniture of provincial quality. A similar chest of drawers bearing the label 'JOHN MITCHEL, Joiner / and Cabinet-Maker, Kendal' and inscribed 'December 24th 1770' suggests this piece is earlier than might commonly be assumed (see: C. G. Gilbert, 'Georgian Provincial Furniture', *Antique Finder*, Sept. 1973, pp.28–34).

PROV: Agnes and Norman Lupton Bequest 1953. [31.386/53]

155

155 CHEST OF DRAWERS
*c.*1790
Mahogany; oak, pine

The hinged top, backed by a galleried ledge, covers a well behind the two top rows of dummy drawer fronts; four cock-beaded drawers with the original locks and oak linings below; quarter-round fluted corner colonettes, shaped bracket feet, brass loop handles (replaced on bottom drawers). Mahogany sides and oak back of framed panel construction, internal corner posts and rails oak, pine dust boards and glue blocks. H.112 (44); W.173 (68); D.56 (22).

This piece can usefully be compared to some of the more conservative designs for bedroom furniture (presses, tallboys and chests) in Hepplewhite's *Guide* (1788) which preserve something of the character of Chippendale's plainer designs.

PROV: Given by the executors of Mrs Dorothy Murphy 1960.
[25.2/60]

CHEST OF DRAWERS, mahogany
By Gillows, Lancaster, 1811
Under Cat. No.505 (illustrated)

CHIMNEY FURNITURE

Andirons, Ash-pan, Curfew, Fenders, Fireback, Fire-irons, Grates, Spark-guards, etc.

156 PAIR OF ANDIRONS
Early 18th century
Brass; iron

The elaborately scrolled base is fronted by a crowned female mask and bust, while the bracket feet are faced with coiled

156

dolphins. The standard centres on a large globe with a diminishing tier of rings and knops above ending in a ball and spire finial. The standard is made up of four components threaded around a stem; iron billet bar sawn off.
H.89 (35).

A very similar pair of andirons from Knole Park, Kent is illustrated in *D.E.F.*, II, p.58, fig.16.

PROV: By descent from the Earls of Lindsey, Uffington House, Lincolnshire, to Lady Muriel Barclay-Harvey; bought 1953. [12.3/53]

157 PAIR OF ANDIRONS
18th century
Brass

The concave triangular bases with scrolled tripod feet, support heavily knopped and ringed hexagonal standards of vase and baluster pattern, headed by a cone finial; no evidence of billet bars.
H.86 (34).

PROV: Given by Charles Roberts, Farfield Hall, Yorkshire 1941. [11.175/41]

158 PAIR OF ANDIRONS
Early 20th century
Wrought iron

The upright standards, backed by plain billet bars, are of elaborately scrolled design headed by ruffled tulip finials.
H.66 (26); W.51 (20).

PROV: K. W. Sanderson; given by H. P. Peacock 1947.
[31.1/47]

159 ASH-PAN
Probably late 18th century
Iron; brass

The shallow rectangular tray constructed of iron sheets bonded by rivets, has a rounded front outlined by a brass lip and base moulding.
W.80 (31½); D.61 (24).

PROV: Methley Hall, Yorkshire; given by the Earl of Mexborough 1957. [33/57]

160 CURFEW
Late 17th century
Brass

The semicircular hood is formed of a brass sheet to which a broad strap handle and deep border strips have been riveted;

the handle and borders, with fold-over edge mouldings, are enriched with a punched pattern of lozenge and shuttle-shapes while embossed reliefs of two swans in a fighting posture are soldered to the front.
H.35 (14); W.44 (17½); D.26 (10½).

A curfew – the name is a corruption of *couvre-feu* – was placed over glowing embers on the hearth to keep the fire in overnight and make it safe.

PROV: Said to come from Hornby Castle, Yorkshire; bought from K. W. Sanderson 1956. [20/56]

161 FENDER
Late 18th century
Brass

Of serpentine form with short returns, the front pierced and engraved with an alternating pattern of anthemion and lotus motifs; plain base moulding, the rim enriched with a pearl-bead.
L.101 (40).

PROV: Probably removed from Parlington Hall to Lotherton about 1905; the Gascoigne gift 1971. [23.8/71]

162 FENDER
Early 19th century
Brass

Of straight fronted design with curved return ends; the front and rounded corners incorporate engraved openwork panels centering on anthemion motifs amid scrolling arabesques alternating with cabled columns and spindle galleries. The cabled top moulding supports pairs of vase finials on the returns for resting fire-irons; plain base moulding raised on lion's-paw feet backed by a skirting plate. The cast components are united by bolts. The fretted panels, base and feet bear impressed numbers ranging from 1–6.
L.132 (52).

PROV: Bequeathed by Dr C. Holland Child 1967 [12/67]

164, 163, 161

162

163 FENDER
Late 19th century
Brass; iron

The straight front and rounded ends are pierced by two continuous vine-trail bands divided by a large, horizontal half-round moulding; ramped sheet-iron bottom plate with corner tray and slots to receive standards; raised on three ball feet (one missing).
L.112 (44).

An identical brass fender is illustrated by L. A. Shuffrey, *The English Fireplace*, 1912, pl. cxiv.

PROV: Lotherton Hall; the Gascoigne gift 1971.   [23.6/71]

164 FENDER
Late 19th century
Brass; iron

The straight front and rounded ends are pierced by two continuous bands of gothic-pattern tracery divided by a large half-round applied moulding; ramped sheet-iron bottom plate raised on three ball feet (two replaced).
L.96 (38).

PROV: Lotherton Hall; the Gascoigne gift 1971.   [23.7/71]

165 FENDER
Possibly by Carron Co, Stirling
*c.*1900
Bright steel; iron

The bow front is perforated by a band of flutes alternating with engraved paterae set between rows of applied studs, with pearl beading above and below; plain base moulding, flat, sheet-iron bottom plate.
L.112 (44).

An identical steel fender is illustrated by L. A. Shuffrey, *The English Fireplace*, 1912, pl. cxiii.

PROV: Lotherton Hall; the Gascoigne gift 1968.   [7.668/68]

166 FENDER AND SET OF FIRE-IRONS
*c.*1903
Bright steel; iron

The straight front with curved returns is faced with a large half-round applied moulding set between horizontal pierced bands enriched with clusters of studs; the ramped sheet-iron bottom plate has corner trays to lodge the fire-irons which are supported by end standards designed to match the implements; plain base moulding raised on three ball feet. Impressed '838'. The shovel, tongs and poker have flattened knob handles with milled bands and the shafts are ringed; the coal scoop is outlined with a perforated panel, the tongs have a faceted pivot plate.
Fender: L.122 (48). Implements: L.74 (29).

PROV: Original to the Drawing Room at Lotherton Hall, built in 1903; Lotherton Hall sale (Hollis & Webb, Leeds) 1–2 Oct. 1956, lot 35 (withdrawn); the Gascoigne gift 1968.   [7.197/68]

169, 167, 160, 168

167 FIREBACK
Early 18th century
Cast iron

The upright rectangular plate has an arched top crested by twin cherub heads with dolphins on the shoulders; the central panel features Hercules, his club beside him, seated on the skin of the Nemean Lion embracing Iole, the couple are observed from behind a tree by a boy. The composition is bordered by a running pattern of tulips and fruit with acanthus scrolls at the base.
H.80 (31½); W.56 (22).

Because of his dalliance with Iole, Hercules' wife Deianira, sent him the poisoned shirt of Nessus, which in the end killed him, after dreadful torments and burnings. The story is told in Ovid's *Metamorphoses*.

PROV: Temple Newsam; given by the Earl of Halifax 1922.
[1922/F59]

168 FIRE-FORK
Possibly 17th century
Iron

Of pitch-fork design with a ferrule; the turned ash shaft is old, but not original.
L.117 (46).

PROV: Said to come from Ledston Hall, Yorkshire; given by K. W. Sanderson 1954. [20.1/54]

169 LOG-TONGS
Possibly 18th century
Iron

The hexagonal stem handle with a knob finial is bolted to a shoulder spring bearing two widely splayed arms with shaft rings ending in cruciform claws which come together to take up logs.
L.91 (36).

PROV: Said to come from Ledston Hall, Yorkshire; given by K. W. Sanderson 1954. [20.2/54]

170 FIRE SHOVEL AND TONGS
19th century, last quarter
Bright steel; ormolu

The shovel has a slightly flared blade centering on a pierced lyre-motif and the stem, ornamented with shaft rings, is headed by a chased ormolu handle of foliated rococo design; the tongs are of similar pattern with squared shoulders and one pivoted limb.
L.80 (31½).

Two sets of steel and ormolu-mounted fire implements from the State Bed and Dressing Rooms were purchased at the Temple Newsam sale, of which only the above set and a second pair of tongs *en suite* survive.

PROV: By descent from the Hon Mrs E. C. Meynell Ingram to the Hon. E. F. L. Wood; bought at the Temple Newsam sale (Robinson, Fisher and Harding) 26–31 July 1922, lot 373 or 407. [1922/F58]

171 SET OF FIRE-IRONS
Late 19th century
Bright steel; brass

The poker, fashioned with a long spike and the shovel, fitted with an axe-shaped blade, have twisted shafts featuring open heart and ring elements; the tongs are of matching pattern and each implement is headed by a cast-brass handle in the form of a lion sejant holding a shield.
L.86 (34).

PROV: Guilsborough Grange, Northampton; bought from Mrs A. Hill 1958. [4/58]

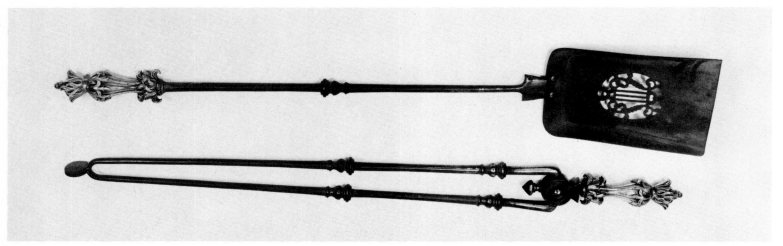

170

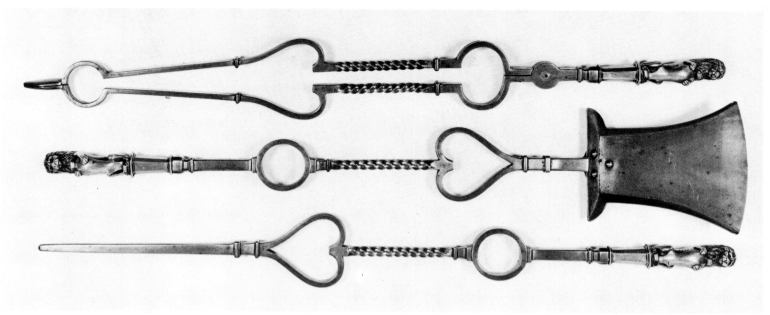

171

172 SHOVEL AND TONGS

By Thomas Elsley, London to the design of C. F. A. Voysey, 1898
Copper

The shovel has a heart-shaped scoop riveted to a straight shaft ending in a baluster and ball handle. The tongs have heart-shaped nippers and the arms, fashioned with slight swellings, are riveted to a U-shaped spring into which the short baluster and ball handle is socketed.
L.65 (25½).

One of three uniform sets from Moor Crag: Brighton Museum and Art Gallery acquired a companion set, the other is privately owned. Illustrated in an undated trade catalogue in the R.I.B.A. Drawings Collection (Voysey, Box XI) titled *Thomas Elsley Ltd, 28 and 30 Grt Tichfield Street, Designs by C. F. Voysey, Architect*, p.1, No.1570 (shown as implements making up a fireside companion). This set of fire-irons featured in the *Arts and Crafts Society Exhibition*, 1902. The Cecil Higgins Art Gallery, Bedford owns a complete fireside companion of this model (M.253).

PROV: Made for J. W. Buckley, Moor Crag, Windermere; his daughter Mrs H. I. L. Speller; bequeathed to Miss D. M. Dixon; bought from the Lotherton Endowment Fund 1976. [23.4/76]

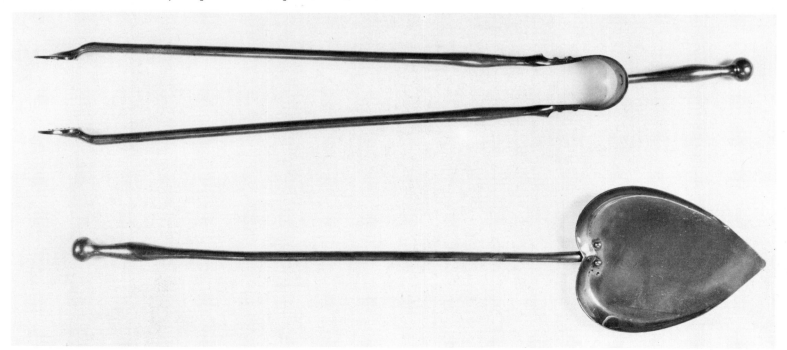

172

173 SHOVEL AND TONGS
*c.*1900
Bright steel

Knopped shafts with acorn terminals; the splayed scoop is pierced with a rose and classical urn design, the tongs have a faceted pivot plate.
L.69 (27).

PROV: Lotherton Hall; the Gascoigne gift 1968.   [7.667/68]

174 FIRESIDE COMPANION
*c.*1900
Brass

The stand has a high domed foot supporting a shaft headed by a cruciform bracket from which the fire-irons are suspended; ring-finial lifting-handle. The implements comprise a shovel, circular hearth brush and sprung tongs with turned wooden handles; poker missing.
H.86 (34).

PROV: Lotherton Hall; the Gascoigne gift 1971.   [23.10/71]

175 BASKET-GRATE
Early 18th century
Iron

The rectangular basket has three front bars supported by pillars with ball finials and a central post; the lateral standards, connected by a bridge rail, are in the form of tall columns mounted on square plinths with ogee bases, each headed by a wrythen flame-finial. The basket is fitted with loose wedge-shaped cast-iron cheeks and the plain back plate rises to an ogee cresting decorated with simple grooves and a finial; the rear structure rests on wrought iron stays.
H.84 (33); W.106 (42).

PROV: The Earls of Mexborough, Methley Hall, Yorkshire; bought 1957.   [32/57]

175, 159, 569

176

177

176 BASKET-GRATE
18th century, second quarter
Iron.

The rectangular basket with ramped cheeks and an ogee back plate, is fronted by three bars supported by blocked corner pillars with ball finials; the splayed standards are designed as tall spiral-twist spires raised on plinths formed of four open columns set on base blocks; wrought iron back legs.
H.79 (31); W.84 (33).

PROV: Methley Hall, Yorkshire; given by the Earl of Mexborough 1957. [31/57]

177 BASKET-GRATE
*c.*1750
Bright steel; iron

Of serpentine fronted design with a pierced Chinese fret pattern apron and square tapering standards, engraved with flowers and leafy scrolls, raised on openwork pedestals fretted to match the apron, with ogee feet; the standards and grate pillars support ball finials. The basket has ramped sides with an ornamental pendant beneath the step; plain cast iron back plate mounted on strut supports.
H.81 (32); W.89 (35).

PROV: Bought from Pratt & Sons 1948. [8.1/48]

178 BASKET-GRATE
Various dates, partly mid 18th century
Brass and iron

178

Although the grate has been assembled from old components it includes some fine metalwork. The serpentine-fronted brass apron of *c*.1765 is pierced and engraved with an elaborate rococo design of paired dolphins and ho-ho birds pecking at fruit amid leafy stems with a central draped urn; the wings are similarly engraved with exotic birds. The tapering brass standards and basket pillars surmounted by urns come from a different grate while the modern wrought iron rear structure and side plates support an early eighteenth century cast iron fireback decorated with a crowned shield bearing the French Royal Arms surrounded by musical and military trophies.
H.94 (37); W.86 (34).

PROV: Bought 1938.   [24/38]

179 BASKET-GRATE
Late 18th century
Brass and iron

The serpentine brass front spanned by three iron bars, has square fluted standards set angle-wise to the basket; the wings and pierced scale-pattern apron are engraved with shuttle motifs and have pearl-beaded borders, the standards and wings support urn finials. The ramped sides and plain arched back plate framing a firebrick are of cast iron, brass castors on the back feet.
H.86 (34); W.86 (34).

PROV: Bought 1938.   [25/38]

180 REGISTER-GRATE
Late 18th century
Iron

Bow-fronted with four bars set between cheek panels crested

by wrythen urn finials; the apron is bordered with studs and three ball ornaments.
H.64 (25); W.74 (29).

PROV: Bought from C. J. Pratt (Antiques) 1944.   [15/44]

181 BASKET-GRATE
By Henry E. Hoole & Co, Sheffield
c.1882
Iron

The S-shaped end supports with ball finials and volute feet raised on base blocks are bridged by a curved bottom rail with four bow-fronted bars above; the front, cast as a single unit, is embellished with pendant husks and foliate scrolls. The back plate, which has an arched fan cresting and ramped sides are lined with fireclay.
H.70 (27½); W.60 (23½).

The front and back castings are impressed with a diamond registration mark and the number '2276'. The Patent Office Registers (BT 44/5) show that the design for this grate, No.387091, was entered on 27 Sept. 1882, Class 1, Bundle 3, by Henry E. Hoole of Sheffield. The Representation is filed under BT 43/53.

PROV: Bought from C. J. Pratt (Antiques) 1944.   [6/44]

179

181

181

182 DOG GRATE
Probably by Thomas Elsley, London
1894
Iron and brass

The rectangular basket-grate, framed by upright bars and tall corner posts with ball finials, has scroll brackets at each end. The base rail is supported on the billet bars of two andirons with massive brass standards composed of spired globes above arcaded blocks raised on scroll bases ornamented with satyr masks amid strapwork. The cast components are threaded on a central stem.
Grate: H.59 (23); W.109 (43).
Andirons: H.94 (37).

Supplied for the dining room at Temple Newsam which was remodelled by Norman & Burt of Burgess Hill to the design of C. E. Kempe in 1894. Thomas Elsley regularly produced iron and brasswork for C. E. Kempe (the bank ledgers of Norman & Burt record payments to Elsley and the St Pancras Ironworks between 1890 and 1895) he provided hardware for the sideboard, Cat. No.343.

LIT: *Country Life*, 8 Oct. 1904, p.528, repr.; F. Moss, *Pilgrimages to Old Homes*, V, 1910, p.329, repr.; C. G. Gilbert, 'C. E. Kempe's Staircase and Interiors at Temple Newsam 1894',

182

L.A.C., No.65 (1969), pp.6–11, pl.5.

PROV: The Hon. Mrs E. C. Meynell Ingram, Temple Newsam; given by the Earl of Halifax 1922. [1922/F54]

183 DOG GRATE
Probably by Thomas Elsley, London
1894
Iron and brass

The railed basket grate, which follows the same pattern as Cat. No.184, incorporates an ash-pan drawer faced with a brass beading, knobs and a simple blind fret. The grate is supported on two andirons with scrolling wrought iron bases headed by brass poppy-heads.
Grate: H.56 (22); W.86 (34).
Andirons: H.40 (16).

Evidence for Elsley's authorship is given under Cat. No. 182.

LIT: F. Moss, *Pilgrimages to Old Homes*, V, 1910, p.305, repr.

PROV: Ordered by the Hon. Mrs E. C. Meynell Ingram for the Darnley Room at Temple Newsam which was re-modelled in 1894; given by the Earl of Halifax 1922.
[1922/F56]

184 BASKET-GRATE
Attributed to Thomas Elsley, London
*c.*1894
Iron and brass

Straight fronted, with three bars and an integral ash-pan faced with a blind-fret pattern and knob handles; the Doric column standards have ball finials and feet. The ramped sides and back are lined with fire bricks impressed 'INGHAM & SONS / WORTLEY / LEEDS' (a branch of the Leeds Fireclay Co.). Supported on andirons matching the pair under Cat. No.183.
H.59 (23); W.72 (28½).

185

The fireplace in the Blue Damask Room was furnished with an identical grate (F. Moss, p.323, repr.). The date and attribution to Elsley are based on the andirons, which match a pair associated with the dog grate (Cat. No.183) believed to have been supplied by the firm in 1894.

LIT: F. Moss, *Pilgrimages to Old Homes*, V, 1910, p.333, repr.

PROV: Ordered by the Hon. Mrs E. C. Meynell Ingram for the Princes Room at Temple Newsam; given by the Earl of Halifax 1922. [1922/F57]

185 DOG GRATE
By Thomas Elsley, London
c.1896
Iron

The shallow basket with short outward curving corner standards is fronted by three wavy bars, has iron cheeks and a brick back supporting an ornamental crest plate. The grate is mounted on a pair of long rails which rest on the billet bars of two andirons, the tall standards wrought with elaborately scrolled bases, a central faceted knop and *fleur-de-lis* terminals. The arched, cast iron fireback, set between pillars, centres on a strapwork cartouche bearing a *fleur-de-lis* with leafy fruiting cornucopia at either side and a sunflower above.
H.74 (29); W.86 (34). Andirons: H.84 (33).

The cresting is backed by a small tablet inscribed 'ELSLEY' in relief; one andiron is impressed 'SC' beneath a crown.

PROV: Ordered by Colonel F. R. T. Gascoigne for the new dining room built at Lotherton in 1896; the Gascoigne gift 1968. [7.663/68]

186 HOB-GRATE
Late 19th century
Iron

The grate is fronted by three wrought iron bars and a top rail with pierced lugs to support a hanging trivet or footman. The cast iron cheeks faced as three panels, each centre on an oval tablet with a beribboned wreath in the upper division and a cruciform fan-motif below. The medallion on the left-hand side features a seated lady in classical robes holding a bird accompanied by a crane; that on the right portrays Hebe with the eagle.
H.60 (23½); W.106 (42).

The Hebe medallion appears in several sculptures by

James Tassie. These are listed in R. E. Raspe, *A descriptive catalogue of a general collection of ancient and modern engraved gems . . .* , by J. Tassie, London, Vol.1, 1791, p.112, Nos. 1316–1322. The title is 'HEBE, the Fair Goddess sitting, and giving nectar to the eagle, perched on an altar ornamented with garlands. Done from a charming picture of *Gavin Hamilton*, at *Rome*, the property of the *Earl of Exeter*.' The other medallion represents Vigilance – a female figure, so identified, with a crane, is reproduced in the exhibition catalogue: *Disegni Veronesi del Cinquecento*, Venice, Fondazione Giorgio Cini 1971, No.19. (Information supplied by Timothy Clifford.)

The cruciform fan motif is repeated on a grate illustrated by L. A. Shuffrey, *The English Fireplace*, 1912, pl.193.

PROV: Given by Leeds City Museum, having come to them with a composition Adam-style chimneypiece, 1939.
[23/39]

186

187 BASKET-GRATE
By Thomas Elsley, London
c.1900
Brass and iron

The serpentine brass front spanned by three iron bars, has square tapered standards set angle-wise to the basket; the wings and pierced apron, which centres on a tablet, are engraved with semi-classical motifs and edged by pearl-beading; the standards and wings support urn finials. The cast iron back, which frames a firebrick, has a lunette cresting ornamented with a pair of winged mermaids sacrificing at an altar, ramped side plates.
H.74 (28); W.70 (27½).

The backplate bears the name 'T. ELSLEY' cast in relief while the firebrick is impressed 'ELSLEY/LONDON'. This model is illustrated in a trade catalogue issued by T. Elsley, Ltd, the Portland Metal Works, London, 1933, p.27 (copy in the V. & A.).

PROV: Bought from C. J. Pratt (Antiques) 1944.   [7/44]

187

188 HOB-GRATE
Early 20th century
Iron

The serpentine hob fronts with rounded inner cheeks are bridged by four wrought iron bars. The side plates, outlined with pearl-beading and a lotus foot moulding, are ornamented with male and female profile medallions on the cheeks; the main panels are embellished with a canopied arch in hybrid gothic-chinoiserie taste, beneath which stand emblematic figures: Justice is represented with scales and a sword while her companion, who holds a spear and a bird perched on a ball may symbolise Mercy. The cover plates missing.
H.59 (23); W.85 (33½).

PROV: Formerly at Heath Lodge, Hampstead; the Gascoigne gift 1971.   [48/71]

189 HOB-GRATE
By Thomas Elsley & Co, London
Early 20th century
Iron; brass

The panelled cheeks, enriched with pearl-beaded and lotus mouldings, centre on oval medallions suspended from tied ribbons with pendant husks below; the ovals enclose reliefs of female figures in classical robes leaning against pedestals,

one plays a lyre; smaller figures of a musician and a soldier ornament the inner cheeks. The grate is fronted by three wrought iron bars and a perforated brass apron, the hob plates have gadrooned borders.
H.54 (21½); W.80 (31½).

This model is illustrated in a trade catalogue issued by Thomas Elsley, Ltd, The Portland Metal Works, London, in 1933, p.43, priced £6 (copy in V. & A.). The same oval medallions feature on hob grates in a catalogue published by the Carron Co., Scotland c.1905 (copy preserved at Lotherton).

PROV: Bought from C. J. Pratt (Antiques) 1944.   [30/44]

189

190 REGISTER-GRATE AND SURROUND
Possibly by Carron Co, Stirling
1903
Bright steel; iron

Of serpentine-fronted design with four horizontal bars set between engraved side panels; the apron, faced with blind fretwork, incorporates a sheet-iron ash drawer. The integral fireplace surround, delicately engraved with festoons and various classical motifs in the manner of Pergolesi, is outlined with pearl beading.
H.52 (20½); W.81 (32).

Displays affinities with Artistic Firegrates in a Carron Company *Architects' Catalogue* of c.1905, preserved at Lotherton.

PROV: Installed when Colonel F. R. T. Gascoigne built the Large Drawing Room at Lotherton in 1903; the Gascoigne gift 1968.   [7.664/68]

191 DOG GRATE AND FIREPLACE RECESS
Probably by Thomas Elsley, London

*c.*1903
Wrought and cast iron; copper

The shallow rectangular basket, fitted with a removable base grille, rests on three cross rails supported by the billet bars of two elaborately scrolled andirons incorporating tulip motifs and headed by pierced copper finials. The splayed grate recess is lined with cast iron panels ornamented with an over-all *fleurs-de-lis* pattern.
H.44 (17½); W.89 (35). Andirons: H.64 (25).

A catalogue issued by Thomas Elsley Ltd, The Portland Metal Works, London in 1933 illustrates lining panels for fireplace interiors of identical design, p.49. The firm supplied a grate for the dining room at Lotherton, Cat. No.185.

PROV: Ordered for the entrance hall at Lotherton, re-modelled by Colonel F. R. T. Gascoigne in 1903; the Gascoigne gift 1968. [7.662/68]

192 DOG GRATE AND FIREPLACE SURROUND
By Lenygon and Morant, London
1912
Bright steel; iron

The surround, embellished with pearl-beaded borders, applied paterae and engraved floral arabesques, is fitted with a draught curtain. The serpentine grate fronted by wrought iron bars has pierced standards set with ornamental balls and conical finials; the apron, engraved to match the surround, is faced with corner paterae. The ramped side grilles are built into the fireback and the front is supported on square tapering legs ending in vase feet enriched with bright-cut engravings.
H.69 (27); W.71 (27).

PROV: Installed when the South East Room at Temple Newsam was remodelled as a Library in the early-Georgian style by Lenygon and Morant 1912; given by the Earl of Halifax 1922. [1922/F55]

193 SPARK-GUARD
*c.*1900
Brass; iron

The rectangular, tubular brass frame with rounded shoulders and two cross stays, supports a wire mesh; a wrought iron grapple attachment, which hooks over the grate bars, is connected by chains to a rod, permitting the angle of the guard to be adjusted. Impressed 'MEKAN PATENT'.
H.43 (17); W.51 (20).

PROV: Lotherton Hall; the Gascoigne gift 1968. [23.9/71]

191

CHIMNEYPIECES

194–8 CHIMNEYPIECES

The provision of chimneypieces was normally entrusted to the architect responsible for designing an interior, the majority being crafted either by a statuary or professional house-carver working under his direction. However, some patrons commissioned them from cabinet makers, which explains why many eighteenth century furniture pattern books include designs for chimneypieces.

The collection at Temple Newsam includes an interesting range of indigenous documented chimneypieces, together with others acquired in recent years either at demolition sales or through the trade. Those at Lotherton Hall mostly date from 1895–1905; they reflect typical revival idioms of the period, but are on the whole unremarkable. The Leeds Art Gallery contains an extravagant bronze chimneypiece and over-mantel commissioned from the sculptor Alfred Gilbert by

Sam Wilson for Rutland Lodge, Leeds in 1912. The history of this Art Nouveau masterpiece was unravelled by Lavinia Handley-Read 'The Wilson Chimneypiece at Leeds, an Allegory in Bronze by Alfred Gilbert', *L.A.C.*, No.59 (1966) pp.10–16.

In view of their ambiguous status – part architectural features, partly furnishings – only the more significant chimneypieces at Temple Newsam are noted in the following narrative survey. The earliest documented specimen was supplied by the statuary John Thorp of Bakewell in 1719: it is of white marble with a scrolled pediment centering on a grotesque satyr mask. Richard Fisher of York provided several handsome carved and painted pine chimneypieces for interiors remodelled by Henry 7th Viscount Irwin between 1738 and 1745, the finest example being installed in the Blue Damask Room. An eminent pair of architectural chimneypieces erected in the Long Gallery by Robert Doe in 1740 are directly copied from an engraved design by William Kent published by Isaac Ware in 1735. The lower stage of each is executed in stone, the overmantels, framing

197

paintings by Antonio Joli, are pine and the putti on top, emblematic of the seasons, are of cast lead. In 1894 Mrs Meynell Ingram commissioned an imposing two-tier armorial chimneypiece for the dining room, based on an Elizabethan original at Hardwick Hall and finally, when the South East Room was remodelled as a library in 1912, Lenygon and Morant provided a chimneypiece designed by Ralph Freeman-Smith in the early Georgian style.

Between 1938 and 1957 seven 'expendable' Victorian chimneypieces were removed and replaced by examples better suited to the existing room schemes. A composite painted pine model centering on a military trophy in the style of Louis XVI was purchased from Thomas Edwards & Son of Harrogate in 1939 for the Chinese Drawing Room (9.49/39). The Green Damask Room contains an interesting early rococo chimneypiece transferred from nearby Seacroft Hall in 1938 (11.2/38) and a late eighteenth century white statuary and yellow Siena mantlepiece, with a fine classical tablet of Venus instructing Cupid, purchased from Pratt & Sons (15/44) was set up in the Terrace Room in 1944. A massive white marble Regency period chimneypiece in the Prince's Room (13.1/57) came from Methley Hall, Yorkshire in 1957 while an imposing Istrian marble example was acquired in the same year from Bridge House, Bury, Lancashire (26/57) and placed in the Darnley Room. It is elaborately carved in the Italian baroque style (Cat.198) and ornamented with shields bearing eagles displayed and medallions inscribed $\frac{A}{B\,D}$ and JVL MCLIII (July 1653).

The design is strikingly similar to a chimneypiece illustrated in the trade catalogue titled *Examples of Furniture and Decoration*, n.d., p.236, No.P.4505 issued by Gillows of Lancaster about 1910. It was presumably ordered from Gillows by Thomas Wrigley & Sons of Bury who built Bridge House as a residence for their mill manager.

The elaborate rococo chimneypiece from Darrington Hall, Essex (27.1/47) purchased from Pratt & Sons for the North West Room (Cat.197) was almost certainly crafted by a furniture maker. The stripped pine frame, with Siena brocatelle slips bordered by statuary marble, was originally painted. Lastly, when the Tudor woodwork from Bretton Hall was installed at Temple Newsam in 1947 a large oak chimneypiece from St Ives, Bingley (25/69) was incorporated in the room scheme. The heavy carved overmantel enclosing four armorial panels painted in *grisaille* appears to be early seventeenth century Flemish or German work, but the pilasters and associated features are much later. The structure is a typical specimen of Victorian antiquarian taste.

CLOCKS

199 LANTERN CLOCK
By Edward Norris, London
*c.*1680
Brass cased

Framed by Doric corner pillars connecting the top and bottom plates, with ball feet and vase finials; fixed back and front plates, hinged side doors; the front and sides are headed by fretted and engraved crestings of crossed dolphin pattern, the whole surmounted by a bell suspended from a rib canopy capped by a finial. The dial centre is finely engraved with a rose and tulip design and inscribed at the top 'Edward Norris

at the Cross Keys (represented pictorially) in Bethelm Londoni fecit'; the silvered chapter ring which overlaps the front plate, is graduated by Roman numerals with quarter and half-hour markings; conventional single hand; the clock is supported on a modern bracket.

Twelve-hour pull wind striking movement with two driving weights on cords and twin clickwork; the original verge replaced by an anchor escapement with a long seconds pendulum (an old conversion); alarm mechanism missing. H.38 (15).

PROV: Given by Miss H. M. Hawkyard 1956.   [32.2/56]

200 LONG-CASE CLOCK
Attributed to Henry Hindley, York
Case *c.*1690, movement *c.*1740
Walnut; fruitwood, oak, pine

The canopied hood designed with a door and side windows is enhanced with walnut mouldings, an ebonized arabesque-pattern blind frieze and black corner columns capped by gilt capitals; the domed cresting and front are decorated with floral marquetry in the Dutch taste; the trunk door, edged with a half-round bead and headed by a convex moulding is elaborately styled with pairs of *amorini* supporting pots of flowers inhabited by birds executed in scorched and green-stained woods; the plinth panel depicts a parrot amid tulips; the compositions are bordered by seaweed marquetry and the case sides are veneered in walnut; solid base, oak carcase.

The square unsigned brass dial with urn and eagle spandrels appears, from scored lines on the back, to be a cut down arch dial plate of *c.*1740 with a later chapter ring and a dummified date aperture. The eight-day horizontal rack-striking movement with anchor escapement, seconds pendulum, original seconds pointer and hands is slightly earlier than the dial which has been adapted to accommodate it. H.221 (87).

The movement displays many features associated with clocks by Hindley of York: double baluster plate pillars, barrels designed without spokes, a star-wheel movement to the striking rack, a knee-shaped hammer and detachable (pinned) arbor pullies.

EXH: *Temple Newsam Heirlooms*, 1972 (24).

PROV: The Ingrams of Temple Newsam; given by the Earl of Halifax 1922.   [1922/F7]

201 LONG-CASE CLOCK
By Peter East, London
*c.*1695
Walnut; fruitwood, oak, pine

Canopied up-sliding hood with reglazed front and side

200

201

201

windows, walnut mouldings and original spiral twist rear colonettes, the front pair replaced, finials missing; styled with floral marquetry in various green-stained and scorched woods on an ebonized fruitwood ground; the trunk door, convex hood mould and plinth panel are fronted with elaborate marquetry compositions of flowers in pots, paired cherubs and a bird; the sides are panelled with walnut veneer; modern bracket base, oak carcase.

Square brass dial ornamented with an engraved surround and second period foliated winged cherub's head spandrels; the matted dial centre with a seconds disc, square calendar aperture and turned winding holes, is set with later steel hands; the chapter ring engraved 'Peter East London' is marked with half- and quarter-hour divisions and small numbers at five-minute intervals outside the minute band. One month striking movement with external count wheel lifting piece, anchor escapement, seconds pendulum and four decoratively turned plate pillars, the dial cut away behind; wooden pulley-wheels renewed.
H.224 (88).

PROV: Given by Mrs A. H. Burkett in memory of the Manbys of Knaresborough 1968. [23/68]

202 LANTERN CLOCK
By Henry Webster, London
*c.*1710
Brass cased

The corner posts with vase finials and ball feet are cast in one piece, fixed back and front plates, hinged side panels; headed on three sides by pierced and engraved arabesque pattern crestings surmounted by a wrought-iron bell cage enclosed by the bell and capped by a vase finial. The dial centre is finely engraved with a vase of tulips and daisies inscribed at the top 'Henry Webster Fecit'. The brass chapter ring which overlaps the plate by a short margin, is graduated in Roman numerals with quarter and half-hour divisions; original single pointer, the clock is backed by a suspension hoop.

Conventional thirty-hour striking movement, both trains being operated by Huygens endless chain system; original anchor escapement and long pendulum. Never equipped with an alarm mechanism.
H.37 (14½).

PROV: Bequeathed by Walter H. Burniston 1977. [30/77]

202a LONG-CASE CLOCK
By John Crucifix, London
*c.*1715
Walnut; harewood, pine, oak

The flat-topped hood, headed by a blind fret has side windows and a glazed door set between corner columns styled with inlaid flutes and gilt capitals; the upper door is enhanced with a floral marquetry trail and the trunk door elaborately decorated with a vase of flowers, female demi-figures amid seaweed and a bird, in various stained and scorched woods on an ebonized ground; the plinth front re-veneered with a conventional walnut marquetry panel; the sides, mouldings and ogee bracket feet painted to simulate tortoiseshell; original glass 'bull's-eye'; oak and pine carcase.

The chapter ring, engraved 'Jno Crucifix London', and foliate satyr-mask spandrels, have been re-set on a new dial plate and the original movement replaced by an early nineteenth century eight-day rack-striking mechanism with an iron falseplate frame incised 'B. WRIGHT & Co' (recorded in Bisset's *Magnificent Directory*, 1808, as factors in Birmingham); the brass back plate is stamped 'C. RENNISON'; the seconds dial and calendar converted; later hands.
H.198 (78).

PROV: Lotherton Hall; the Gascoigne gift 1968.
[7.145/68]

203 MURAL CLOCK
18th century, second quarter
Pine; oak

The large octagonal face cut from an oak board, is set in a broad moulded frame decorated at the angles with gilt fronds on a black japanned ground; the pine trunk is enclosed by an arcaded door outlined by a bead and japanned with a scene of four oriental figures in a garden, the surround and sides are similarly styled with borders and floral swags in the Chinese taste; brass escutcheon and hinges; a service opening, on the

right side of the movement, was formerly closed by a door, the back board is slotted for hanging.

The white painted dial boldly marked with Roman and Arabic numerals is pierced by a winding hole; original brass hands with spade pointers, the minute indicator counterbalanced. Tall, narrow eight-day single train plated movement of London quality with anchor escapement and seconds pendulum, the lead weight encased in brass.
H.140 (55).

LIT: *L.A.C.*, No.97 (1975) p.25, fig.3.

EXH: Temple Newsam, *Back-stairs Furniture*, 1977 (3).

PROV: This clock, originally designed for hanging, probably in the servants' quarters at Temple Newsam, was later built into a high niche in the kitchen wall (now a passage leading to the chapel); the 1808 Temple Newsam inventory records in the kitchen 'A dial clock'; given by the Earl of Halifax 1922.   [1922/F50]

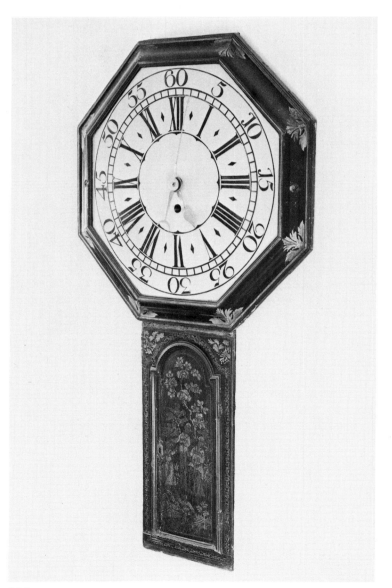

203

204

204 MUSICAL BRACKET CLOCK
By John Hodges, London
*c.*1735
Oak; pine

The movement is contained in a bell-topped case with turned brass finials, lifting handles and carved corner trusses of double-scroll design; the front arch and side panels frame openings (to emit the chimes) fitted with gilt card pierced by arabesque patterns with red fabric behind; moulded base on low bracket feet, glazed front and solid rear door (replaced); the scarlet japanned case is richly decorated with chinoiserie borders, reserved floral panels, garden scenes with boys playing and bird roundels.

The arched brass dial has a silvered oval tablet engraved 'John Hodges LONDON' above the mock pendulum aperture, a square calendar window and three winding holes in the matted centre; looped steel hands; there are two subsidiary dials inscribed 'Strike/Silent'; 'Chime/Not Chime' and, in the arch a third disc engraved with three tunes selected manually by pointer 'The Happy Clown / Grenadiers March / A Rigadoon'; cast brass spandrels of female figure head and bird design, the arch is set with sphinx-pattern ornaments. The back plate is finely engraved with paired birds, masks and a basket of fruit amid scrolling arabesques centering on a trumpeter. This three train eight-day clock plays at the hour one of three tunes; the eight bells, fifteen hammers and pin barrel are ranged at the side of the movement; spring driven verge escapement with half-second bob pendulum; the calendar apparatus, minute hand and small pointers are not original.
H.81 (32).

Large numbers of English scarlet japanned clocks were exported to Europe during the reign of George II; the repairers' marks and provenance indicate this model is of continental extraction 'E. Slag / J. A. Molin / L. Greuzau – 1882 / Eskilsfunci – 1937'.

LIT: *Connoisseur*, June 1970, p.143, repr.

PROV: Collection in Stockholm; Ole Haslunds Hus Ltd, Copenhagen; Pelham Galleries, London; H. Blairman & Sons; bought with the aid of a government grant 1970.

[15/70]

205 LONG-CASE CLOCK

By Thomas Ogden, Halifax, Yorkshire
The movement c.1740, case c.1800
Oak; mahogany, pine

The hood, of scrolled pediment design faced with mahogany, has a central ball finial and plain corner columns; the oak trunk is styled with mahogany bands, stringing lines and fluted corner colonettes; square bracket feet, pine back board.

The arched brass dial, surrounded by a plain bead and engraved with an elaborate composition of foliage and scrolling tendrils, has a silvered chapter ring, marked at the half-hours with *fleurs-de-lis* and inscribed around the lower edge 'Thos Ogden De Halifax', a subsidiary seconds dial, applied ringed winding holes and date aperture; the arch contains a rotating globular 'moon' parti-coloured silver and black, figured with a numerical age scale and pointer; original steel hands. Eight-day (horizontal) rack-striking movement with anchor escapement and six ornamental plate pillars; the lunar globe is actuated by a vertical shaft geared from the motion work; the seconds pendulum has a pine shaft, weights encased in brass.
H.236 (93).

Movements with this type of lunar indicator were mistakenly known in the north as 'Halifax' clocks. The true

205

205

'Halifax' moon is a rotation disc which shows pictorial phases of the moon through a small circular hole in the dial where a seconds indicator is usually placed.

The original clock case was thought 'not to have any artistic merit' and a new oak and ebony case was made by Marsh, Jones and Cribb of Leeds in 1906 to the design of W. Swindon Barber, architect (photograph in files); in 1944 the movement was married to the present late Georgian case.

LIT: S. Hamer, 'Long Case Clocks and Local Makers', *Halifax Antiquarian Society Reports*, Nov. 1921, p.221; D. Barker, 'Thos Ogden de Halifax. An 8-day revolving Ball Moon Long Cased Clock, *c*.1740', *Antiquarian Horology*, Vol.9, No.5 (Dec. 1975), pp.545–50, figs.1–10.

PROV: The Old Assembly Rooms Halifax; J. Whiteley Wood (who commissioned a new Edwardian case); Mrs Alfred Holden; Roger W. Tolson of Coley, Yorkshire who bought the present case in 1944 from Jackson Antiques, and bequeathed the clock to Leeds in 1973.   [36/73]

206 LONG-CASE CLOCK

By Robert Higgs, London
c.1750
Oak; pine

The arched hood with side windows and engaged corner columns is surmounted by a flattened bell-top with turned finials and a fretted panel in the cresting; the plain trunk enclosed by an arched door edged by beading is raised on a square plinth with base mouldings; the whole case is japanned with gilt chinoiseries on a black ground, the sides and hood being decorated with floral panels and borders, while the door and plinth are fronted by Chinese figures and birds amid garden buildings in gold, silver and crimson, outlined with diapered frames and spandrels.

206

The arched brass dial has a matted centre, with a silvered seconds ring above the original steel hands and a square calendar aperture; the arch is set with a circular silvered tablet engraved 'Rob't Higgs LONDON' flanked by cast dolphin ornaments, the brass spandrels feature classical heads amid scrolls. Conventional eight-day rack-striking movement with anchor escapement and seconds pendulum; internally toothed date disc.
H.236 (93).

PROV: Given by Lady Martin 1957. [12/57]

207 LONG-CASE CLOCK

By Joseph Hallifax, Barnsley, Yorkshire
*c.*1750
Oak

The square-topped hood is finished with a straight moulded cornice surmounted by a board profiled to suggest a canopied cresting; the frieze is supported at the front by thin pillars and the rear corner boards are shaped to simulate baluster turned columns; the trunk, raised on a box plinth, has a flattened bell-top door fixed by staple hinges.

The square brass dial is mounted with cast urn and eagle-pattern spandrels, the matted centre is pierced by false winding holes and a lunette calendar indicator; the chapter ring, signed around the bottom 'Joseph Hallifax Barnsley', is marked at the half-hours with *fleurs-de-lis*; hands not original. Thirty hour rope-driven movement with pull wind, count wheel striking, anchor escapement and seconds pendulum, the dial plate cut away behind the chapter ring.
H.201 (79).

PROV: Given by Mr and Mrs E. Askham 1958. [9.1/58]

208 TAVERN CLOCK

By William Scafe, London
*c.*1760
Pine

The arched top is crested with carved and gilt bunches of grapes between urn corner finials and the large face, flanked by Doric pillars, is signed below the dial 'Wm Scafe, London', the short box trunk, enclosed by an arcaded door, is fitted with scrolled corner brackets of open foliate design and terminates in a coved base supporting a grape pendant; the case is japanned in the Chinese taste on a black ground the front being gilt with diapered patterns, floral borders and small reserved panels enclosing exotic birds and seated figures; the door portrays a garden scene of three men in European dress seated at a table being served with drinks; the columns are treated to simulate marble. Pine case with windows at either side of the movement, one enclosed by a door the other by a sliding panel; key escutcheon and seconds hand replaced.

207

Eight-day timepiece with a four wheel train, conventional recoil anchor escapement and a centre seconds movement; heavily constructed owing to the large weight required to drive the seconds train; screwed through a falseplate to the dial back, additional support provided by a modern seat board.
H.195 (77).

The japanned drinking scene and carved grape ornament indicates this clock was made to hang on the wall of a tavern.

PROV: Agnes and Norman Lupton Bequest 1953.

[13.377/53]

208

209 PEDESTAL ORGAN CLOCK
By George Pyke, London
c.1765
Ebony; rosewood, oak, pine, beech, etc

The clock case is supported on a large square pedestal veneered with ebony and banded by brass mouldings; the peninsular corners are set with grained rosewood console trusses carved with fronds and shells in the style of William Kent, while the front, which opens as a door, and each side panel, are faced with mirror plates; the frieze is decorated with gilt bronze lion's-masks, pierced foliated strapwork plaques and rosettes, the surbase bears satyr-mask mounts. The clock case, like the pedestal, has peninsular corners; it is rasied on pairs of scrolled ormolu feet and the plinth, which is banded with looking-glass, supports four brass corner columns with an applied floral trail twisting around the shafts headed by Corinthian capitals and leafy-urn finials, ormolu rosettes decorate the base blocks. The domed front and side elevations, veneered in ebony and banded with brass beads, are set with elaborately pierced gilt-bronze mounts in the rococo taste incorporating floral sprays and female-masks, while the hood is surmounted by a cast figure of Mercury. The glazed front is framed by a brass surround and the arched side doors are filled with matching pierced and chased gilt-bronze panels reminiscent of Berain's designs. The compositions centre on a strapwork cartouche enclosing a musical trophy and *lambrequin* motif surrounded by an elaborate open system of floral festoons, arabesques, flaming urns, grotesque faces and female-masks headed by a basket of flowers. The clock case is enclosed behind by arched double doors fitted with a lock and bolts.
H.254 (100); W.96 (38); D.69 (27).

The small white enamel dial with two winding holes and original pointers is set in a spacious painted landscape showing a village dance in the foreground, some of the figures being animated. Two violinists and a cellist move their bows; an old man rises from his stool and nods with the music; a woman tells the fortune of a girl and a knife-grinder operates his wheel. In the middle distance a dog chases a duck across the river and rushing water turns a mill wheel, while men and farm animals pass over a bridge. In the top distance sailing ships cross an estuary through moving waves. A formation of ormolu plaques below the clock face represents, in perspective, the Seven Muses grouped on a terrace flanked by urns and statues of Diana and Apollo on pedestals.

The clock mechanism is a conventional English bracket fusee movement with anchor escapement and hour striking independent of the organ; the motionwork articulating the figures lies behind the dial plate, while the gear causing the barrel to revolve is behind the backplate. The organ consists of three registers, two of pine one in tin, each of twenty pipes tuned at 8, 4 and 2 ft. pitch governed by three manual stops (Flute, Principal and Piccolo). There are eight tunes, selected on a numbered dial at the side; there is also an 'Off/Play' pointer. The sheepskin leather bellows are pumped by a connecting rod attached to an extended 8 in. flywheel, the whole being driven by a massive lead weight that descends

209

into the pedestal. The music, selected from the following eight tunes, is discharged every two hours:

Pretty Polly Hopkins
Drops of Brandy
Unidentified
Life Let us Cherish
Mrs Whitmore
Why Ever don't you come
Bergère Legère (Manimet)
Sicilian Mariner's Hymn

The tune selection dial is engraved by the maker 'George Pyke / Bedford Row / London' and the sound board is inscribed 'March 1765' which approximates to the assumed date of production. Other names and dates occur on the mechanism, including, on the clock movement 'Sept. 6/1886 B. Janz'; 'A Chalut 1899 / London' and 'A Hunzinger / London 1904'. The music barrel is signed 'Jos Gurk Fecit / Dublin 1817', he probably re-pinned the cylinder. The organ discloses 'John Eborall / June 8th 1845'; '27 Oct. 1864 T. Thomas'; 'A Ams / July 8th 1878 / No 1 Bedford St. Holborn; 'Z. Furdezer / Borugh High St / 20: XII: 1904' (the clock was last restored by David Barker and the organ by Peter Wood in 1975).

209

209

This organ clock relates significantly to a family of musical clocks built by Charles Clay, and others signed by George Pyke, author of this model. Little is known about Pyke except that he or his father John completed an ambitious organ clock left unfinished at Clay's death in 1740 and a label has been recorded 'All sorts of machines and other organs made and sold by Geo. Pyke, Maker to His Majesty. Facing Bedford Row' (L. G. Langwill & N. Boston, *Church and Chamber Barrel Organs*, 1970, p.62). The fullest available account of their products is contained in two *Country Life* articles by E. Croft Murray, 'The Ingenious Mr Clay', 31 Dec. 1948, pp.1378–80 and 'Musical Clocks by Charles Clay', 21 April 1950, pp.1112–14. The spectacular clock completed by Pyke was exhibited by Clay's widow in 1743 and a contemporary press notice preserved in *Lyson's Collectanea* (British Library 1889 e 5) records that it featured a figural plaque below the dial precisely identical to the gilt casting on the Temple Newsam clock, and furthermore, that it was modelled by John Rysbrack:

'At the entrance of each Avenue is represented in Sculpture the Genii of the Arts and Sciences as Painting, Sculpture,

Geometry, Musick, Architecture, Arithmetic and Astronomy . . . they are made of Silver in Alto Relievo by Mr Rysbrack; and are reposing on a Piece of Architecture in Basso Relievo, made of Brass, in true Perspective'.

Identical plaques appear on the famous clock by Clay named 'The Temple of the Four Grand Monarchies of the World' in the Royal collection at Kensington Palace; it also occurs on several other organ clocks by Clay: one is at Castletown, Ireland (*Antique Collector*, Aug. 1974, p.29); another was sold by Christie's, 8 Nov. 1973; a third was sold by Christie's in Geneva (*Country Life*, 4 Jan. 1973, p.25, fig.3). The decorative side grilles are repeated on clocks by Clay in the Royal Palace of Naples, another formerly at Hall Barn, Beaconsfield (Christie's, 29 Sept. 1969, lot 6) and the example at Castletown. The organ clock by Pyke in the London Museum (Joicey gift Acc. No.60.34) not only possesses the same side panels and figurative tablet, but rests on a strikingly similar pedestal decorated with many identical mounts. There is yet another smaller version by Pyke at Wentworth Woodhouse, Yorkshire; Birmingham Museum and Art Gallery have an especially important model by Clay signed 'The first made in Perfection NI'.

Nicholas Goodison has pointed out that in 1765 John Fothergill advised his partner Matthew Boulton to visit Pyke's workshop to inspect methods of gilding metal. The fine chasing and gilding of the ormolu mounts on this clock case indicate Pyke's expertise. (*Ormolu: The Work of Matthew Boulton*, 1974, p.22).

LIT: *Country Life*, 21 Dec. 1951, p.2105, repr.

PROV: According to information supplied by the donor the clock is reputed to have belonged to Marie Antoinette, was acquired by the Duke of Buckingham at the Tuileries sale, taken to Dublin when he was Viceroy and included in the Stowe sale (1848). The provenance thus far remains unconfirmed but its later history is trustworthy: given about 1860 by Sir Morton Peto to George Parker Bidder, grandfather of Mrs Ina Kitson Clark who bequeathed it to Leeds 1954   [27/54]

210 LONG-CASE CLOCK
By Dollif Rollisson, Halton, nr. Leeds
*c.*1770
Oak; mahogany, pine, beech

The hood, of broken segmental design, has fluted corner columns with gesso-gilt beech capitals and bases; the trunk, set with fluted corner colonettes and enclosed by a saddle-top door, rests on a panel fronted plinth supported by square bracket feet; the solid oak case is styled with simple mouldings and plain mahogany crossbanding; pine backboard and internal structures, finials later.

The arched brass dial engraved around the top 'DOLLIF ROLLISSON HALTON', has a two-month moon phase

210

210

mahogany panels and banding on an oak ground; the door is inset with a foliated lozenge; modern bracket base; oak and pine carcase.

The unsigned arched dial has flower and shell rococo pattern spandrels with a silvered sun in splendour mounted between brass dolphins in the arch; matted dial centre with a seconds pointer, calendar aperture and steel hands; half and quarter-hour divisions marked; cut away plate behind the chapter ring. Conventional eight-day rack-striking movement with anchor escapement and seconds pendulum. H.224 (88).

PROV: Lotherton Hall; the Gascoigne gift 1968. [7.158/68]

212 LONG-CASE CLOCK
By John Goodchild, Bradford, Yorkshire
*c.*1785
Oak; mahogany, pine

The hood has a scrolled cresting faced with veneer and stamped brass terminal discs, fluted and ebonized columns with brass mounts and rear corner boards profiled as balusters; the trunk, enclosed by a saddle-topped door, is styled with fluted colonettes headed by a blind fretwork band; the box-plinth, fronted by a raised panel, has chamfered and fretted corners and a foot moulding; the oak case is crossbanded with mahogany; pine backboard and internal structures; finials missing.

The arched brass dial, inscribed around the top 'JOHN GOODCHILD BRADFORD' has a two-month lunar phase indicator with numerical age scale; the disc, painted with moons, a scene of the crucifixion and a pastoral landscape, is eclipsed by geographical lunettes; the dial centre is engraved with classical foliage and a rayed date dial; cast brass rococo pattern spandrel ornaments, the dial plate cut away behind the chapter ring, steel pointers replaced. Conventional pull wind thirty-hour chain driven movement with count-wheel striking, anchor escapement and seconds pendulum. H.214 (84).

PROV: Given by Mr and Mrs E. Askham 1958. [9.2/58]

indicator with numerical age scale; the disc, painted with lunar orbs and landscapes, is fronted by hemisphere and rising sun lunettes; the dial centre is engraved with free rococo foliage, a twelve-rayed seconds dial and date pointer; cast spandrels of elaborate rococo pattern; original steel hands. Conventional eight-day rack-striking movement with anchor escapement.
H.234 (92).

The seatboard is inscribed 'ROLAND', and the bell 'F. Dawson April 1832'.

PROV: Given by W. Uttley 1954. [6/54]

211 LONG-CASE CLOCK
*c.*1775
Oak; mahogany, rosewood, pine, sycamore

Arched hood, the scrolled pediment ornamented with brass discs and finials, the central ball supporting an eagle; the front is set with fluted corner colonettes and faced with mahogany crossbanded in rosewood; the trunk, styled with fluted quarter columns, and the box plinth are veneered with

213 TEMPLE CLOCK
By Benjamin Vulliamy, London
*c.*1791
Marble; ormolu, porcelain

The circular movement is enclosed in a white marble balloon-shaped case with an ormolu finial, surround and plinth. The lower stage is designed as a half-round Greek temple fronted by four marble columns with ormolu capitals and bases, the frieze is inset with an ormolu band and surmounted by four classical urns. The portico, raised on a stepped marble pedestal, is backed by a gilt-copper plate chased to represent an archway, in front of which stands a robed female figure in

biscuit porcelain: the Muse of Music playing a flute, with a musical score at her feet. She leans on a truncated pillar, the group is mounted on an ormolu plinth inscribed 'Vulliamy LONDON No.246'.
H.49 (19½); W.30 (11¾).

The unglazed white enamel dial with gold numerals has the original pierced and chased gilt-brass pointers, one winding hole and a pendulum adjustment aperture below the XII. The circular, single train movement has a tic-tac off-set escapement, the brass backplate is engraved 'Vulliamy London / No.246' encircled by a garland and the pendulum bob bears the stamp '246'. The rear opening is enclosed by a domed circular brass dust-cover.

The Vulliamy records do not begin until 1797 when the firm had reached No.296; however, from J. T. Cranmer Byng (*An Embassy to China: Lord Macartney's Journal 1793–4*, 1962, p.360, n.12) we learn that clock No. 253 was made for the Emperor in 1792–3 which indicates that the Temple Newsam timepiece dates from *c*.1791. The biscuit figure was supplied by William Duesbury of the Derby porcelain factory; it is taken from a group usually numbered 217, an example of which is in the V. & A., C.309–1940, the modeller is unrecorded (information from Timothy Clifford). Henry Rubin owns an identical temple clock by Vulliamy with a two train movement No.242.

A temple clock of the same design type, No.304 was auctioned at Sotheby's 5 Dec. 1958, lot 103. The cost analysis in the Vulliamy Clock Book in the Royal Horological Institute records:

304	*Small Marble Temple Clock*			
	Day the Marble	6	0	0
	Bullock the Movement	5	15	6
	Culver engraving the hands		5	0
	Amedros the back plate engraving	2	10	0
	engraving border in the frieze		15	0
	engraving the scroll		3	6
	Haas the ring		2	6
	Crockett the gilding	8	18	0
	Huguenin the brass work 28 days	7	0	0
	Long & Drew the dial		16	0
	Duesbury the figure			

PROV: Ballinclea, Co. Dublin, Ireland; by descent to Lord Talbot De Malahide, Malahide Castle, Co. Dublin, Ireland; the Malahide sale, Christie's, 10 May 1976, lot 56; Frank Partridge & Sons; Hotspur, Ltd; bought with the aid of a government grant 1977.   [18/77]

214 BALLOON BRACKET CLOCK
By James Stewart, Glasgow
c.1795
Satinwood; tulipwood, holly, mahogany, pine

213

214

The circular cove-topped case is elevated by a waisted plinth inset with a sand-shaded shell medallion on a green-stained ground; the front is crossbanded in tulipwood between ebony and box strings and the rear door set with a perforated brass grille backed by velvet; brass bracket feet, urn finial; the carcase is built of mahogany staves and pine veneered in satinwood.

The white enamel dial, with matching steel diamond-pattern hands, is inscribed 'STEWART GLASGOW' and enclosed by a convex glass door. Eight-day movement with a star-wheel jump and rack strike, a centrally mounted bell, anchor escapement and half-seconds spherical bob pendulum; the circular backplate is finely embellished with bright-cut engraving in the neo-classical taste.
H.53 (21).

EXH: Temple Newsam, *English Clocks*, 1949 (75).

PROV: Percy Webster (Antiques); given by Frank H. Fulford 1939. [9.48/39]

214

215 MURAL CLOCK
Early 19th century
Mahogany; pine

The case, designed for a wall niche, has a large octagonal face bordered by fluted mouldings and composition rococo scrolls, the box trunk enclosed by an arched door is also styled with fluted corner mouldings; the ornamental details were originally gilt, but the whole case was later grained and is now painted grey.

White enamel dial with plain steel pointers. Eight-day single train movement with anchor escapement, the cushion pendulum bob faced with copper.
H.117 (46).

This clock was formerly set in a niche in the servants' hall at Temple Newsam, the bohemian case, almost entirely of mahogany, may well have been built and dressed-up by the estate joiner.

PROV: The Ingrams of Temple Newsam; given by the Earl of Halifax 1922. [1922/F51]

216 LONG-CASE CLOCK
By John Barraclough, Haworth, Yorkshire
*c.*1815
Oak; mahogany, satinwood, pine

The cresting is of scroll design with circular stamped brass terminal mounts and a central spired ball finial; the hood, with brass mounted corner colonettes, and the trunk, headed by a dentil cornice, are enhanced with chequered tooth

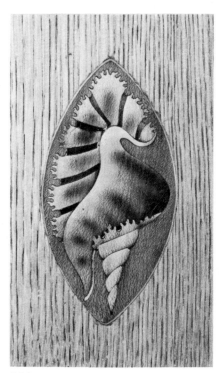

216

strings and satinwood bands; the hump-topped door and plinth panel are inset with shell and seaweed medallions on green-stained grounds; square bracket feet; stamped brass escutcheon and knob; the case is mainly of oak with mahoany facings and decorative bands, pine backboard.

The arched enamel dial plate is inscribed above the hands 'BARRACLOUGH HAWORTH' and headed by an oval painting of a sportsman in a landscape, the dial centre is decorated with a pair of exotic birds and the spandrels with colourful floral sprays; original match stamped crown pattern hands and date pointer. Thirty-hour chain driven movement with pull wind, count wheel striking, anchor escapement and seconds pendulum.
H.236 (93).

The decorative bands and the oval shell-marquetry inset were probably obtained ready-made by the clockcase maker from a wholesale supplier.

PROV: Given by Mrs E. C. Carlton of Leeds 1958.   [10/58]

217 LONG-CASE CLOCK
By Joseph Cheetham, Leeds
*c.*1815
Oak and mahogany; pine, satinwood

The hood has a scrolled pediment with stamped brass terminal discs, three spired ball finials and fluted corner columns mounted with brass collars; the saddle-topped trunk door bears an inset medallion of Britannia with her lion and Union Jack shield, the flag being of post union with Ireland (1801) design; fluted corner colonettes with ebonized base and capital rings; the plinth panel is banded with diagonals centering on a patera; square bracket feet; oak carcase with pine backboard and inner structures, the front partly mahogany faced outlined with crossbanding and strings with decorative details in satinwood.

Arched white enamel dial with Arabic numerals headed by an oval painting of three frigates and inscribed across the middle 'Cheetham Leeds'; rayed spandrels, unmatched stamped brass hands, date and seconds pointers. Conventional eight-day rack-striking movement with anchor escapement and seconds pendulum.
H.231 (91).

PROV: Temple Newsam; given by the Earl of Halifax 1922.
[1922/F60]

218 LONG-CASE CLOCK
By John Galloway, Leeds
*c.*1820
Oak and mahogany; pine, rosewood, satinwood

The scrolled hood with baluster and ring-turned corner columns is veneered with mahogany crossbanded in rose-

217

wood; the trunk enclosed by a saddle-topped door is patterned with mahogany panels defined by rose and satinwood borders; chamfered corners inlaid with ebony strings; the oak plinth faced with decorative surrounds is raised on French bracket feet united by an apron.

The arched enamel dial plate inscribed across the centre 'JNO GALLOWAY LEEDS' is painted with pansy spandrels and a rustic fruitseller in the lunette, original match stamped hands, seconds and date pointers. Conventional eight-day rack-striking movement with anchor escapement and seconds pendulum.
H.234 (92).

PROV: The 'Irwin Arms' tavern, Halton, Leeds; given by John Smith's Brewery Co, Tadcaster 1937.   [21/37]

219 LONG-CASE CLOCK
By Jonathan Carley, Thetford, Norfolk
*c.*1830
Oak; pine, elm

The hood has a bell-shaped cresting faced with three fluted pilasters headed by brass balls; the plain trunk, styled with reeded corners and enclosed by an arched door has a box base raised on square bracket feet. Both doors are mounted with stamped brass key escutcheons in the form of a shield surmounted by an eagle holding floral festoons.

The white enamel dial with gilt roses in the spandrels is inscribed 'J. Carley Thetford'; date and seconds pointers, original match pattern hands. The arch is painted with a lake scene featuring a swan with an animated neck that rocks. Eight-day, rack-striking movement, an extension wire from the anchor escapement arbor animates the swan; fitted with an iron falseplate impressed 'WALKER & HUGHES / BIRMINGHAM' (in partnership as dial makers between 1815 and 1835). The flat steel pendulum rod has a brass faced bob incised 'SWAN' on the back.
H.208 (82).

Jonathan Carley is recorded in Norfolk trade directories from 1830–36.

PROV: From a vicarage in Lincolnshire; bequeathed by Sir George Martin 1976.   [51.32/76]

220 BRACKET CLOCK
By Barber, Cattle & North, York
c.1830
Mahogany; ebony

The arched case is veneered in mahogany and inlaid with brass strings and simple gothic motifs; the sides are panelled with scale-pattern grilles backed by blue paper and mounted with cornucopia ring-handles; glazed rear door; the plinth,

styled with an ebony ripple border and brass inlay, is supported on cast ball feet. The circular white enamel dial with steel pointers and a strike/silent indicator is inscribed 'BARBER CATTLE & NORTH / YORK'.

Eight-day spring driven rack-striking movement, the backplate engraved with the maker's names in cursive script; anchor escapement and half-seconds pendulum fitted with a micrometer adjustment; strike repeat lifting piece with cord attachment. The case is impressed (twice) '8311'.
H.41 (16).

A bracket clock with an almost identical movement and case at Weston Hall, Yorkshire, signed 'Duncan / St James' / London', suggests that the York firm purchased this clock from a supplier, possibly Thwaites of London who reached No.8311 in 1829.

PROV: Lotherton Hall, the Gascoigne gift 1968.   [7.213/68]

221 LONG-CASE CLOCK
By John C. Elliott, Leeds
*c.*1845
Mahogany; rosewood, pine

The scrolled hood centres on a platform with double baluster corner columns at the front backed by profiled board pillars; the trunk has chamfered corners and the door is styled as a hollow arched panel, headed by an ogee cresting with oval insets outlined by rosewood crossbanding above and below; the wide plinth centres on a circular recessed panel, French bracket feet joined by a shaped apron; the veneered carcase and internal structures are of pine with a solid mahogany door and sides.

The arched enamel dial plate is inscribed across the middle 'J.C. ELLIOTT LEEDS' and headed by a lunette painted with a girl harvester, the spandrels are decorated with rustic cottages and the dial centre set with seconds and date pointers; match stamped crown-pattern hands. Conventional eight-day rack-striking movement.
H.236 (93).

PROV: By descent to G. T. Abram, Leeds who presented the clock 1964.   [27/64]

COMMODES

222 COMMODE
Probably by John Channon, London
*c.*1750
Mahogany; oak, pine

Fully serpentine front and sides with canted corners and square bracket feet set at an angle; fitted with two short above three long graduated drawers; the edge of the top and

222

plinth are banded with brass gothic-pattern frets in-filled with pitch and the crossbanded border is defined by a brass string; the front corners support rich ormolu mounts headed by Nereid consoles with rococo foliage, falling water, shells and grotto formations below; the feet are ornamented with scrolling leafy mounts and the drawers set with flamboyantly styled and pierced escutcheons of rococo design; brass locks and castors, the back pair having leather rollers. Veneered in mahogany with a panelled oak back, top, corner trusses and drawer linings; pine bottom, sides, internal braces and dustboards faced with oak rails; unlaminated oak drawer fronts, the bottoms are of framed flush-beaded panel construction.
H.89 (35); W.140 (55); D.69 (27).

222

A small ivory tab fixed in the top right drawer is inscribed 'Oak Drawers / S.E. Bedroom / Southwick' and the lock on the top left drawer is lightly scratched 'Old Drawers / S.E. B.R. 1st / 2 Keys'.

This impressive commode belongs to an exclusive group of George II brass inlaid furniture discussed by J. F. Hayward in the *Victoria & Albert Museum Bulletin*, Jan. 1965, pp.10–23 and April 1966, pp.64–70. It relates to a small sub-group within the main family consisting of five boldly shaped cabinet pieces, all of which reveal similarities in construction, are decked with ormolu mounts of identical design and can be dated to *c*.1745–55. The closest parallel is a serpentine commode in the Fitzwilliam Museum, Cambridge, with exactly corresponding mounts (M.27 1961); a striking writing cabinet in the Arthur Bull collection (*D.E.F.*, I, p.144 fig.45) has Nereid corner mounts and rococo handles of identical pattern coexisting with engraved brass inlay and other ormolu enrichments; a spectacular double bureau dressing-table, half of which is in the V. & A. (W.4–1956),

also features Nereid consoles and escutcheons which must have been cast in the same moulds, the repertoire of ormolu includes bearded heads and a pair of dolphins; finally the

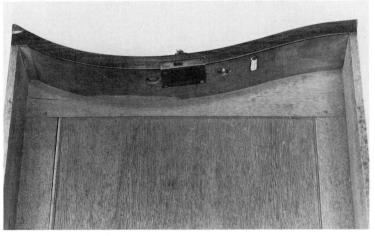

222

handles are repeated on a commode illustrated by P. Macquoid, *Age of Mahogany*, p.146, fig.128. Evidence for the authorship of this group is provided by a pair of massive rosewood bookcases at Powderham Castle, Devon bearing brass tablets inscribed 'J. Channon 1740'. The cabinets are elaborately styled with engraved brass inlay, an uncommon and highly specialized decorative technique which connects them with the group described above, permitting a cautious attribution to the same firm.

John Channon was an Exeter cabinet maker who moved to London in about 1737 and established a workshop in St Martin's Lane, but little is known about his activities.

LIT (only directly relevant references are cited): *Country Life*, 18 Oct. 1956, pp.891–3, figs.1–4; *Antique Collector*, Aug. 1958, p.124 repr.; R. W. Symonds, 'An English Commode of Rare Design and Quality', *L.A.C.*, No.39 (1958), pp.3–8, repr.

PROV: By descent from Lt. Col. Evelyn W. Thistlethwayte, Southwick Park, Southwick, Hants (whose ancestor subscribed to Thomas Chippendale's *Director*, 1754) to his nephew H. F. P. Borthwick-Norton whose widow Eva, sold it at Harrods Sale Room 29 May 1956; Temple Williams Ltd; bought with a contribution from the Harding Fund 1957.   [28/57]

223 COMMODE
*c.*1760
Mahogany; oak, pine

The front is fully and the sides half-serpentine with a moulded top; bold corner trusses of double-scroll design forming short legs on voluted stump feet, the upper scrolls carved with a fronded cabochon; containing three graduated drawers, the fronts cockbeaded and shaped to the curved angle trusses, the base of the lower drawer is faced as an apron with a

gadrooned border and leafy spandrels, which also decorate the sides; the top drawer incorporates a baize-covered writing slide with partitions and two small drawers below; bronze loop handles cast in the rococo taste, ornamental keyhole escutcheons missing. Veneered in mahogany, with solid trusses and a mahogany dressing drawer; oak top, slide and drawer linings with laminated fronts; pine sides, back and dust boards faced with oak rails. A strip has perhaps been cut from the back of the top and the dressing drawer possibly refitted.
H.87 (34½); W.127 (50); D.56 (22).

The mounts are identical to a set (with intact keyhole escutcheons) on a commode reproduced *Apollo*, Vol.58 (1953) p.100, fig. iv which suggests they were stock patterns supplied to the London furniture trade. A commode of identical design but with different brasses is illustrated in *Antique Collector*, 1950, p.148, fig.10.

LIT: *Connoisseur*, Sept. 1919, pp.17–18, fig.v; M. Harris & Sons, *A Catalogue and Index of English Furniture*, II, No.258; *Burlington*, Feb. 1968, p.99, fig.54; *L.A.C.*, No.61 (1968),

pp.5–7, fig.2; C. G. Gilbert, *L.G. & R.F.*, 1971, p.14, repr.

PROV: Mr & Mrs Mango, Kensington; Christie's, 26 June 1924, lot 149; M. Harris & Sons; Sir George Duncomb, Wood Hall, Herts; bequeathed to Lord Deramore of Heslington Hall, York from whose widow it was bought (Lady Martin Bequest Fund) 1967.   [19/67]

223a COMMODE
c. 1760–65
Mahogany; pine, oak

Of serpentine-fronted design with double doors, concave sides and curving, keel-edged corners ending in short scroll feet. The top is rimmed by a brass acanthus moulding and the sides are mounted with ovals wrapped round by a leaf-twist; the doors frame pierced and engraved gilt brass grilles centering on circular fronded whorls surrounded by an open system of scrolling foliage, husks and rococo shells; the flat grilles are backed by panels of blue callimanco and bordered by enriched mouldings. The shaped base is outlined by leafy gadroons centering on shells and acanthus

223a

224

224

clusters; all four corners are set with elaborate gilt brass knee mounts composed of shells and cabochon motifs amid fronded scrolls connected by husk festoons to large acanthus sheaths ending in faceted toes. The top and doors are veneered on to oak and mahogany respectively and the ends on to a pine foundation; the bottom board, panelled back and three adjustable shelves resting on saw-edge supports are of pine; brass pin-hinges, bolts and lock.
H. 89 (35); W. 131 (53½); D. 79 (31)

This commode is one of a pair, the companion being in the V. & A. (W. 32–1977); there is a difference of two inches in their respective widths. No relevant documentation has so far been traced amongst the Dropmore papers at the British Library or the Grenville archive at Buckinghamshire Record Office; the Boconnoc deposit at Truro awaits investigation.

Despite their individual character the commodes are not intimately related to any published groups of English furniture apart from a lavish serpentine commode at Windsor Castle which lacks the brass grilles but bears identical corner mounts (G. F. Laking, *Furniture of Windsor Castle*, 1905, p. 76, pl. 14). The royal commode can tentatively be ascribed to Vile and Cobb who favoured this ambitious yet restrained form combined with rich carvings or mounts and oval panels. They are perhaps the most likely authors of the present pair; the fact there is no Grenville reference in Cobb's bank account is not strictly relevant.

Scraps of crimson silk behind the grilles indicate that the blue callimanco, now faded to ivory, is not original; it dates from about 1800 and may have been inserted to match an upholstery scheme when the commode was installed at Dropmore.

LIT: *Christie's Review of the Year*, 1977, p. 55

PROV: According to an apparently sound family tradition the commode was owned by William-Wyndham Grenville, Bt., prime minister to George III, who acquired and greatly enlarged Dropmore, Buckinghamshire in 1792, although it must originally have been commissioned for another house. Lord Grenville died childless in 1834; his widow survived until 1864 when her property devolved on Lord Grenville's nephew, the Hon. George Matthew Fortescue (d. 1877) of Boconnoc, Cornwall; the commode passed by direct descent to John Bevill Fortescue (d. 1938) and so to his son George whose widow Olive Joan Fortescue moved to Ethy House, Cornwall. On Mrs Fortescue's death her executors, with the agreement of the beneficiaries, Lady Margaret and Lady Elizabeth Fortescue, offered the commode to the government in lieu of capital transfer tax and, following acceptance, it was allocated to Leeds City Council in 1978.
[2/78]

224 COMMODE
*c.*1780
Harewood; satinwood, rosewood, tulipwood, burr walnut, ebony, box, mahogany, pine

Serpentine front with chamfered corners, splayed concave sides and a shaped apron supported on four square tapered legs and decorated overall with engraved marquetry designs in various natural, shaded and green-stained woods on a harewood ground; the crossbanded top is inset with a half-round fan patera and divided into three radiating panels framing arabesque and floral ornament in the neo-classical taste; the frieze is embellished with scrolled foliage on a ground of satinwood and the double doors enclosing shelves figure a roundel containing a trophy (emblematic of sculpture) flanked by classical motifs; the sides display urns surrounded by husk festoons and the legs are inlaid with panels rising to fluted pilasters headed by oval paterae; the back is of framed panel construction. Pine carcase except for the shaped mahogany front rail; brass lock, hinges and flush bolts.
H.85 (33½); W.142 (56); D.52 (20½).

The trophy, composed of a book, a telescope, a ruler, compasses, set-square, protractor and chalk holder also occurs on two French commodes and almost certainly derives from an engraving, although the precise source has not yet been identified. One of the related commodes, owned by Lord Burton, has not been published but the other, from the Frick collection, is reproduced in F. Watson, *Louis XVI Furniture*, pl.23. It was made by Roger Vandercruse in 1769 for the bedroom of one of Louis XVs daughters, Madame Victoire, at Compiègne, and a contemporary description of this piece refers to the relevant trophy as representing the theme of Sculpture.

Hepplewhite observed that commodes of this type were 'adapted for a drawing-room; within are shelves, which answer the use of a closet or cupboard . . . and being used in principal rooms, require considerable elegance'.

The underside is inscribed in pencil 'E.A. Webster / this commode Repaired / 16th Oct. 1933 / Johnstone & Aitchison, / Buccleuch Street / Melrose'. According to information supplied by Mr Webster in 1968 the firm of cabinet makers for whom he worked regularly repaired furniture for local landed families; the interesting possibility thus arises that this commode was made in Scotland.

LIT: *Antique Collector*, Aug. 1940, p.33, repr.; *Apollo*, Aug. 1941, p.32, repr.; G. de Bellaigue, 'English Marquetry's Debt to France II', *Country Life*, 20 June 1968, p.1690; C. G. Gilbert, *L.G. & R.F.*, 1972, p.30, repr.

PROV: John Bell (Antiques) Aberdeen; given by Frank H. Fulford 1939.   [9.44/39]

225 COMMODE
Probably by Edwards and Roberts, London
*c.*1880
Mahogany; satinwood, rosewood, harewood, oak, etc.

The bowed front, fitted with three graduated drawers, is flanked on each side by a convex cupboard enclosing shelves, panelled ends; the top is decorated in marquetry with a large green-stained leaf fan, floral festoons and paired cornucopia in various coloured woods on a mahogany ground bordered with satin and rosewood; the drawers centre on a lyre and

225

crossed palms below floral swags, while the door panels are outlined with satinwood ovals enclosing a classical vase of flowers and scrolling foliage; the six supports headed by harewood pilasters faced with floral pendants terminate below in square tapered legs with satinwood stripes and spade feet. Mahogany carcase with panelled back, oak drawer linings and rails, the marquetry delicately enriched with penwork; cast laurel-swag loop handles, ornamental key. H.92 (36½); W.129 (51); D.54 (21¼).

On the evidence of style and provenance it is possible this sophisticated Adam Revival commode was supplied by Edwards & Roberts of Oxford Street, who specialized in high class commercial furniture. Edmund Leatham certainly purchased a card table (Cat. No.555) and almost certainly a set of dining chairs (Cat. No.102) and a superior marquetry bedroom suite from this firm.

A Sheraton period satinwood commode in the V & A (636–1870) appears to have served as the model for this example. During late Victorian days it was not uncommon for cabinet making firms to copy furniture in the National collection.

PROV: Acquired at the time of his marriage in 1883 by Edmund Leatham, Wentbridge House, Yorkshire; inherited by Lady Gascoigne; the Gascoigne gift 1968.

[7.133/68]

226

226 COMMODE
By Gillow & Co, Lancaster
1907
Walnut; kingwood, sycamore, oak etc.

Of rectangular break-front design containing two deep drawers faced with a square panel which appears to overlay the front; the frieze is divided into three shallow drawers, the middle section being enriched with a guilloche band in ormolu; the central panel, decorated with a vase of flowers in marquetry of various stained and shaded woods on a sycamore ground, is set with a fronded pineapple base mount; the concave sides and drawer fronts are styled with walnut panels enhanced with corner rosettes and outlined by ormolu mouldings, kingwood borders and strings; the canted corner posts headed by console mounts terminate in fronded lion's-paw feet; laurel pattern ring handles elaborated with ribbons; the top supports a Breccia Corallina marble slab; veneered

on to an oak carcase. The upper lock, operated by an ormolu key featuring interlaced L's, secures both main drawers.
H.89 (35); W.140 (55); D.56 (22).

This piece exactly duplicates a well known early Louis XVI French commode in the V. & A. (Jones Collection, 1087-1882). An identical model is illustrated in a trade catalogue titled *Examples of Furniture and Decoration by Gillows* (n.d. *c*.1905–10) p.102 captioned 'P.3351 Late Louis XV Commode, with richly chased bronze mounts, mercury gilt; marquetry panel to door; fine marble top. A faithful reproduction of the notable piece in the "Jones" collection'.

PROV: Bought by Sam Wilson from Gillow & Co. for the drawing room at Rutland Lodge, Leeds, July 1907 and entered in his notebook as '1 Jones Commode with fine Marqueterie Panel & rich ormolu mounts £190'; the Sam Wilson Bequest 1925.   [S.W.220]

227 COMMODE

By Gillow & Co, Lancaster
1907
Purplewood; tulipwood, harewood, walnut, oak, ash

Of rectangular design with bevelled forecorners and straight tapering legs; the front contains two drawers faced as a single panel of trellis-pattern marquetry enclosing quatrefoil motifs, outlined with brass beading and crossbanded tulipwood borders; the end panels are of matching design and the front rail centres on a lunette apron set with an ormolu rosette above crossed laurel sprays; the angles are mounted with floral pendants and the drawers, fitted with ring handles backed by rosettes, are both secured by the upper lock; ormolu key; purple Marmo Fior marble top. The carcase is of oak and ash veneered with purplewood crossbanded in tulipwood; the marquetry panel is figured in walnut and fruitwood on a ground of harewood.
H.89 (35); W.92 (36½); D.51 (20).

This commode duplicates one in the V. & A. (Jones Collection, 1101–1882). The reproduction model is illustrated in a trade catalogue titled *Examples of Furniture and Decoration by Gillows* (n.d. *c*.1905–10) p.104, captioned 'Q443 A Louis XVI Commode in Mahogany richly inlaid with Marquetry: Marble top: Bronze mounts, Mercury gilt. A reproduction from the "Jones" collection'.

PROV: Bought by Sam Wilson from Gillow & Co in 1907 for the drawing room at Rutland Lodge, Leeds and entered in his notebook as '1 fine Louis XVI commode with ormolu mounts £130'; the Sam Wilson Bequest 1925.

[S.W.226]

227

228 COMMODE
By Gillow & Co, Lancaster
1907
Walnut; mahogany, sycamore, box, oak

Semi-circular with a Breccia Corallina marble top; in the form of a *meuble d'entre deux*, containing two deep drawers in the front with a shelved cupboard enclosed by a curved door at each end and a central frieze drawer; raised on four square tapered legs headed by pilasters with inlaid flutes surmounted by ormolu fruit swags; the main drawers and door panels are faced with marquetry representing an inter-laced trellis design in mahogany and sycamore enclosing small floral motifs on a walnut ground; the frieze is inlaid with Vitruvian waves and the panelled legs are embellished with ormolu corner cables, foliate toe and cap mounts; laurel pattern ring handles and wreathed escutcheons, the upper lock secures both drawers. Veneered on to an oak carcase.
H.87 (34½); W.79 (31); D.39 (15½).

PROV: Bought by Sam Wilson from Gillow & Co in 1907 for the drawing room at Rutland Lodge, Leeds and entered in his notebook as '1 Louis XVI Commode marqueterie & ormolu mounts £120'; the Sam Wilson Bequest 1925.
[S.W.225]

229

228

229 COMMODE
By Gillow & Co, Lancaster
1907
Purplewood; tulipwood, walnut, pear, oak, ash

Of bow-front design with curvilinear splayed sides and a panelled frieze faced with ormolu guilloche mounts contain-ing a central drawer; the two main drawers and side panels are veneered in purplewood with crossbanded tulipwood and walnut borders, the bottom drawer is fronted with twin *brule parfum* and integral apron mounts; the rounded pilasters are headed by ormolu oak swag consoles and the hipped cabriole legs with fronded husk mounts terminate in lion's-paw sabots; the principal mounts are backed by stained pearwood insets; laurel pattern ring handles and oval escutcheon, both drawers being secured by a single lock; veneered on to an oak carcase with ash drawer fronts; Diaspro Brecciato marble top. The handles are stamped '3673' and the lock plate '1471'.
H.86 (34); W.112 (44); D.53 (21).

This commode is almost identical in design and styling to three French transitional models by Charles Topino reproduced in J. Nicolay's *L'Art et La Manière des Maitres Français*, fig. AE; Sotheby's *Catalogue of the René Fribourg Collection VII*, 17–18 Oct, 1963, lot 803; and the Mentmore Sale, Sotheby's 18–20 May 1977, lot. 511, repr.

PROV: Bought by Sam Wilson from Gillow & Co in 1907 for the drawing room at Rutland Lodge, Leeds and entered in his notebook as '1 Louis XVI Commode £70'; the Sam Wilson Bequest 1925.
[S.W.221]

230

230 COMMODE
*c.*1910, with earlier skeleton
Satinwood; mahogany, pine, tulipwood, harewood, box, etc.

Of semi-elliptical design, the front divided by stiles into three framed panels with a central door, four short splayed legs bridged by shaped aprons, veneered in richly figured satinwood crossbanded in tulipwood and inset with floral marquetry; the top is fronted by a wide mahogany border enriched with a ribbon and stem design, the frieze is decorated with floral swags and the stiles with husk chains headed by urns; the three curved panels frame identical vases of flowers in vividly stained woods, the door being enhanced with corner sprays; single shelf within. The top, panels and legs veneered on to mahogany, pine back, bottom, shelf, rails and laminated frieze. Under edge of door incised 'B'.
H.85 (33½); W.122 (48); D.40 (16).

The mean proportions, poorly conceived and executed marquetry work, shoddy construction and existence of heavy stain indicate that this commode is spurious. The stiles are veneered on all four sides showing that a pier table has been embellished and converted by the insertion of panels etc., into a cabinet. The exactly repeated marquetry patterns and general stylistic character are consistent with a date of about 1905–10. Edwardian trade catalogues such as H. Lebus, *Furniture Designs*, n.d. *c.*1909, p.310 illustrate a wide range of similar 'reproduction' satinwood cabinet furniture.

PROV: Given by Frank H. Fulford 1939. [9.43/39]

CUPBOARDS

Clothes Presses, Gun, Hall, Hanging, Table-Leaf, Wardrobes, etc.

231 CUPBOARD (OF 'CREDENCE' TYPE)

*c.*1530
Oak

The lower stage of splay-fronted 'credence' form, contains a cupboard and two drawers with a partly enclosed space below; the shelf is backed by a narrow ledge supporting a tall reredos originally surmounted by a canopy and the whole, elaborately carved structure, is built into wall panelling; the back frames two tiers of three panels divided by carved and spired gothic columns, the upper row is sculpted in high relief with the heads of two men and a lady set in arcaded niches; the lower panels are heraldic centering on the arms, helm, crest and initials 'T.W.K.' for Thomas Wentworth, Knight, of West Bretton flanked by the arms of Dronsfield (left) and Fitzwilliam of Mablethorpe (right) amid various Renaissance grotesques and arabesques; the two cupboard doors are boldly carved with half-length figures of courtly musicians set in architectural niches with lateral screens of lozenge-head and linen-fold panels framed by rails and stiles decorated with guilloche, imbricated and foliate diaper designs; the drawer fronts are ornamented with leafy dolphins; the wrought iron strap hinges and elaborate latch locks are nineteenth century. The structure was probably originally free-standing.
H.249 (98); W.152 (60); D.51 (20).

It is clear that this dresser has been re-built several times and only fragments of the canopy (visible in a photograph in *Old Furniture*, Nov. 1927, p.99) now survive; the lower stage has been shortened at the base and enclosed by linen-fold panels, it originally had open sides and a plinth platform. However, the basic structure conforms to a standard early Tudor design type and the carved work is definitely of Renaissance vintage; its age is confirmed by documentation. Two slightly earlier cupboards at St William's College, York (J. B. Morell, *Woodwork in York*, 1949, pl.134) and a French example (E. Mercer, *Furniture 700–1700*, 1969, pl.73) although displaying a different decorative programme confirm the integrity of the structural form.

Stylistically this dresser and the companion bed (Cat. No.3) are intimately related to a small group of early Renaissance woodwork probably carved in England by continental craftsmen. The Salkeld screen, erected in Carlisle Cathedral in 1542, offers striking analogies, particularly in the Tudor Perpendicular enrichment of the engaged columns, the profile medallions and hybrid Anglo-Italianate decorative detailing. It may be significant that Sir Thomas Wentworth leased some land from the Bishop of Carlisle in 1542 as work on the screen was about to start. The overall character of both commissions suggests Anglo-Flemish workmanship.

LIT: J. Hunter, *South Yorkshire*, 1831, II, p.249; *Old Furniture*, Nov. 1927, pp.96–100, repr.; *Country Life*, 9 July 1938, pp. xxxvi–viii, repr.; *L.A.C.*, No.2 (1947) pp.5–8, repr.; *L.A.C.*, No.68 (1971) pp.5–16, repr.; P. Brears, 'The Renaissance Furniture from Bretton', *L.A.C.*, No.70 (1972) pp.13–17, repr.; P. Brears, *Yorkshire Probate Inventories 1542–1689*, Y.R.S., Vol.132 (1973) pp.1–3, 83–6, 145–53.

PROV: Evidence of the original ownership of this dresser and the companion bed (Cat. No.3) is provided by armorials; the central achievement and initials refer to Sir Thomas Wentworth, Knight Marshal of Bretton; the Dronsfield arms acknowledge the descent of the Bretton estates from this family through marriage and those of Fitzwilliam allude to his grandmother's ancestry. The year before his marriage in 1531 Sir Thomas built a new timber-framed hall at Bretton for which this furniture was made since both pieces are recorded in an inventory following his death in 1542 (Y.A.S. DD. 70/85). They stood in the 'lytle chamber', the 'bedstead' being equipped with opulent hangings and coverlets: '. . . a fether bed A bolster a pair of arras A teister of russet velvet and clothe of golde with dropps of golde upon the velvet. A quylt of yellow taffeta lyned with blew bokeram Two newe keveringes of arras lyned with white canves A quylt of gren and red sarcinet with thredes of golde lyned with redd and gren bockeram . . .'. The dresser is more briefly described: 'In a cubborde within the said chambre Thre Bittes . . . A pair of Stirrops a pair of spurres guilt A Bottell . . . and a pair of armyng showes'. In another inventory of Bretton Hall, dated 1638, the bed and cupboard were not itemized, but their existence 'in the Inner Parlour' where there were 'Cuartaines with vallance and cubard cloth' is implied. When in about 1650 the Wentworths built a larger mansion on a new site at Bretton the woodwork from the oak chamber was installed in a room described in an inventory of 1675 as the 'King Henry Parlor' (Y.A.S. DD. 70/85). Once again there is no direct mention of either piece but their presence is indicated by the entries: 'Furniture for a bedd' and 'One Carpitt for a Cubbard'. About 1720 Sir William Wentworth rebuilt the Hall as a fine classical mansion, the King Henry Parlour being once again incorporated into the scheme; here the furnishings were seen by Joseph Hunter, author of *South Yorkshire*, 1831 who described the bed and cupboard in great detail and recounted the family tradition that Henry VIII had slept in the room – an association which doubtless explains why these antiquities were cherished so piously. Hunter also states that the carved heads were reputed to portray Henry VIII, the Earl of Southampton and Cardinal Pole; they are however more likely to represent Sir Thomas and members of his family. The estate passed by descent to Viscount Allendale who, before selling Bretton Hall, gave the panelling and furnishings of the King Henry Parlour to Leeds for insertion in an early Tudor room at Temple Newsam 1947.   [4.2/47]

Note

The associated wall panelling reveals five different linen-fold patterns with a further five minor variants and four

231

different frame mouldings; the frieze is built in sections carved with guilloche, foliate diaper designs and dolphin arabesques. This panelling, together with a row of nine low-relief profile medallions of helmeted warriors, prelates and court ladies, doubtless came from more than one interior in the original house, being amalgamated to fill out the room at Bretton in which the ornamental woodwork was installed in the eighteenth century.

232

232 HALL CUPBOARD
1685
Oak

Of framed panel construction united by pegs, the corner posts, rails and stiles banded with grooves; the plain lower stage is enclosed by double doors each divided into three panels with a narrow shelf above; the upper doors are vigorously carved with a fronded interlace design and the projecting frieze rail, set with turned corner pendants, is enriched with relaxed foliate scrolls and inscribed '1685 p^M_M'; the dentil cornice, top and back boards renewed in pine; modern locks and fastenings; original pin-hinges; internal structures of peeled and riven timber; some annotated joints; the top left-hand corner block is lightly incised 'BM' – presumably the initials of a later owner.
H.152 (60); W.125 (49); D.59 (23).

This cupboard is a typical example of Westmorland furniture, the carved decoration being closely related to fixed woodwork in the area – for instance the pulpit in Kirkby Lonsdale church and also movables at Townend, Troutbeck. There is a very similar example at Barbon. A craft refinement peculiar to the region is the inside through chamfer on members framing the main panels. These cupboards were often built into the wall of a farmhouse living room, which may account for the later pine backboards. The initials indicate this piece was a wedding present, the top letter identifying the couples surname, the two below being for their Christian names.

EXH: Temple Newsam, *Oak Furniture from Lancashire and the Lake District*, 1973 (11).

PROV: Bequeathed by Mrs Emma Read, Leeds 1965.
[15.7/65]

233 HALL CUPBOARD
1705
Oak; sycamore

In two stages separated by a ledge; the upper part having a pair of doors carved with a low profile system of stylized foliage and flowers flanking a fixed central panel enriched with spirals; the projecting frieze bearing turned pendants and chequered insets at either end, is decorated with a vine-trail centering on the initials RSM and date 1705; the frame members are styled with a flat undulating pattern of scrolling arabesques. The lower part, containing two heavily moulded drawers running on side bearers above a cupboard enclosed by two doors each formed of three fielded panels, is less richly carved than the top stage, but inset with obliquely chequered and dogtooth bands. The corner posts serve as legs; plain sides of fielded panel construction; plank top and back; the upper cupboards enclose a narrow and the lower a broad shelf. The bottom doors are fitted with H-pattern and the top with pin-hinges; two original wrought iron locks remain; modern knobs.
H.173 (68); W.137 (54); D.48 (19).

The door panels are ingeniously contrived with an inside chamfer on members framing the main panels, a technical refinement paralleled on the well-known American group of Hadley chests some of which also display a very similar combination of formalized decorative elements and flat lobed scrolling patterns. The carved decoration is characteristic of north Lancashire, an origin consistent with the known provenance. The distinctive scrolling arabesque formula is repeated on the pulpit dated 1684 at Over Wyresdale in the Trough of Bowland and there are allied cupboards at Towneley Hall (dated 1706); Astley Hall; Turton Towers and Rufford Old Hall, all in Lancashire. Many other examples can be cited. Anthony Wells-Cole has pointed out that this cupboard belongs to a late sub-group within the tradition which can be traced back to the 1650s.

233

LIT: *Country Life*, 27 Sept. 1973, p.868, fig.3; A. Wells-Cole, 'An Oak Cupboard made in Lancashire', *L.A.C.*, No.73 (1973), pp.19–20, repr.; C. G. Gilbert, 'Regional Traditions in English Vernacular Furniture', Winterthur Conference Report 1974, *The Arts of the Anglo-American Community in the Seventeenth Century*, ed. P. Quimby, pp.51–3.

EXH: Temple Newsam, *Oak Furniture from Lancashire and the Lake District*, 1973 (12).

PROV: Dr H. O. Pilkington of Preston; auction sale (E. J. Reed & Son, Preston) 7 April 1920; M. Goldstone & Son; bought with the aid of a government grant 1973.   [7/73]

234 HANGING CORNER CUPBOARD
18th century, first quarter
Pine

Of quarter-round design containing three shelves enclosed by double doors japanned in black and gold with a Chinese allegory. The left-hand door panel features a lady standing in a palace landscape with a doe in the foreground, the right-hand panel bears a similar scene with a seated mandarin and a stag; the compositions are united by a diapered arch. Original brass lock plate, one of the pierced butterfly-pattern hinges replaced, the interior is painted black.
H.94 (37); W.57 (22½); D.39 (15¼).

PROV: Bequeathed by Sir George Martin 1976.   [51.24/76]

TABLE-LEAF CASE, mahogany
By Gillows, Lancaster, 1810
Under Cat. No.497 (illustrated)

CLOTHES PRESS (WARDROBE), mahogany
By Gillows, Lancaster, 1811
Under Cat. No.506 (illustrated)

GUN CUPBOARD, mahogany
By Gillows, Lancaster, 1811
Under Cat. No.507 (illustrated)

CLOTHES PRESS OR WARDROBE, papier-mâché
Birmingham, *c*.1851
Under Cat. No.518 (illustrated)

235 CLOTHES PRESS OR WARDROBE
19th century, second half
Oak, pine

Of upright rectangular design containing six sliding trays enclosed by double doors and raised on blocked lion's-mask front feet with bun feet at the rear; the cornice is set with lion's-head corbels. The doors and ends are of framed panel construction each side being composed of six carved panels of uniform parchemin design. Both the doors are fronted by

234

six panels, the top two tiers centering on heads set in roundels; the full countenance displays a top row with two saltire panels in the middle flanked on the left by one featuring paired scrolls and stylized foliage and on the right hand by a cone motif with dolphins in each corner. The row beneath is of varying parchemin pattern with leafy berried sprays in the spaces while the bottom panels are decorated with a simple parchemin design and lack profile roundels; foliate base moulding. The back, top and bottom boards are of pine, the hinges are impressed: 'HUXLEY / & CHING' and the lock is stamped 'BRAMAHS / SECURE / LOCK'.

H.203 (80); W.152 (60); D.64 (25).

The structure combines old and new work, the frame members, sliding trays and carved ends are modern, whereas the door panels, lion's-head corbels and feet are of sixteenth century date. The central pair of medallion heads in the middle row are reproductions which have been let into old panels to complete the sequence of roundels.

PROV: The Wentworths of Bretton Hall, Wakefield, Yorkshire; given by Viscount Allendale 1947.   [4.5/47]

235

236 CUPBOARD
*c.*1865
Oak

Designed in the form of a chest with a fixed lid fronted by three panels centering on an heraldic shield flanked by cupboard doors and with a long projecting frieze drawer. The frieze, faced with quatrafoils enclosing florets, is lipped by drop tracery and the chamfered door panels are enriched with flamboyant tracery and naturalistic ornament; each end panel bears a parchemin pattern surrounded by herbs; the corner posts, styled with hollow chamfers containing florets, are extended as legs and headed by blocks carved with dog-tooth and pineapple pendants; the central roundel bears a shield amid flowers and foliage depicting the arms of Cooper impaling Mann.
H.77 (30½); W.114 (45); D.46 (18).

The achievement represents Cooper of Dowbiggen, Yorkshire 'Gules, on a chevron between three lions passant argent, three lozenges gules' impaling Mann of Linton, Kent 'Sable, on a fesse embattled between three goats passant three roundels sable'. The frieze is carved with two sets of initials ISC/FC and the pierced quatrafoil spandrels enclose shields lettered IS and C – these initials presumably relate to members of the Cooper family. During the next century this class of furniture rapidly degenerated into 'Stockbroker Tudor'.

PROV: Bequeathed by Mrs. L. I. Wright 1965.   [14.1/65]

237 CLOTHES PRESS OR WARDROBE
Probably by Collier and Plucknett, Warwick
*c.*1880
American oak; cedar of Lebanon, pine, ash

The tall central section, containing a cupboard enclosing five sliding trays with four long drawers below, is flanked by narrow hanging cupboards each fitted with a high shelf and brass pegs; the breakfront is headed by an arch enriched with a waterleaf border and foliate spandrels with a spindle gallery above bearing two carved finials of seated lions holding shields; the forecorners are styled with spiral turned columns with leafy capitals set between fluted pilasters and the side wings support straight, heavily moulded cornices. The panelled door fronts, outlined with moulded beading, are painted with heads, vases of flowers and birds representing the seasons on a gold ground: the upper row portrays a girl with a daffodil; a red headed youth; a negress wearing a peacock headdress and a girl holding a lily, the roundels being inscribed 'SPRING / NORTHWIND / SOUTHWIND / SUMMER' respectively; the lower panels display appropriate bouquets of flowers and fruit standing in antique vases; a kingfisher and robin occupy lozenges beneath a carved demi-lunette pattern band on the side doors. The sides are similarly panelled, but plain, and the cabinet rests on a plinth base. The gilt bronze strap-hinges are incised with zig-zag bands; cast drop and loop handles; brass locks stamped 'IMPR LEVER LOCK'; the hanging cupboards are lined with calico.
H.272 (107); W.178 (70); D.64 (25).

Tyntesfield, near Bristol, the original home of this piece still contains furniture labelled by James Plucknett of Warwick and Laverton & Co of Bristol. Elizabeth Aslin (q.v.) attributes it to Collier & Plucknett, on the evidence of stylistic analogy with proven pieces in the collection; other painted cabinets underpinning her ascription have since been recorded. The paintings are in the manner of J. Moyr Smith, but no engraved source has so far been identified.

LIT: E. Aslin, *19th Century English Furniture*, 1962, pl.89; H. Schaefer, *The Roots of Modern Design*, 1970, pl.144.

PROV: By descent from Matilda Gibbs of Tyntesfield, Bristol to her grandson George Richard Gibbs, 2nd Baron Wraxall; Christie's, 18 July 1968, lot 320; H. Blairman & Sons; bought 1968.   [23.2/68]

237

236

238 HANGING CORNER CUPBOARD
*c.*1900
Mahogany; pine

The three ogee-fronted shelves are enclosed by a single door glazed with a pattern of hexagons and squares; the pilasters and frieze outlined with obliquely chequered strings, interior stained black, the cornice not original.
H.102 (40½); W.74 (29); D.44 (17½).

PROV: Bequeathed by Sir George Martin 1976.   [51.26/76]

239 COMMODE CLOTHES PRESS
*c.*1925
Mahogany; oak, pine

The upper stage contains five sliding trays enclosed by veneered double doors faced with crossbanding and outlined by an astragal panel with leafy corner clasps; the dentil cornice is headed by an elaborately carved and pierced cresting centering on a rococo cartouche and the coved forecorners are styled with floral festoons. The bombé lower part, fitted with two short above two long drawers, has massive frond-carved corner trusses ending in knurled feet, the bottom rail being enriched with a foliated waterfall motif. The doors have flush bolts and a brass bead, while the drawers are mounted with bridge handles. The carcase is largely of mahogany with a pine back, top, bottom and dust boards; oak drawer linings, mahogany trays.
H.221 (87); W.157 (62); D.66 (26).

The design corresponds closely to the left-hand side of a commode clothes press illustrated on pl. cvi in the first edition (1754) of Chippendale's *Director* (pl. cxxxi in the third edition) the source however lacks a decorative cresting. This item provides a classic instance of furniture being expensively faked to imitate a celebrated Chippendale pattern book piece. The basic carcase is a late eighteenth century clothes press of plain straight-fronted design which

239

239

has been built up to create a bombé lower stage with elaborate corner trusses and other embellishments; the doors were also appropriately faced and the corners improved by wedding a suitably carved strip to the outer edges, finally an ambitious cresting was added to the simple late eighteenth century dentil cornice. Although the conversion and decorative treatment have been skilfully performed, the construction, inconsistent evidence of wear, tell-tale scars and a poor colour confirm the dubious provenance. Another, better known version of this *Director* design formerly in the Mulliner collection (*D.E.F.*, II, p.165, fig.20) perhaps inspired this fake; a third model in the Cooper Union Museum was illustrated in *Connoisseur*, Vol.128 (1951) p.65.

LIT: *Country Life*, May 1938, p.548, repr.; *Apollo*, July 1938, p.17, fig. vii; A. Coleridge, *Chippendale Furniture*, 1968; pl.274.

EXH: Temple Newsam, *Pictures and Furniture*, 1938 (108); Temple Newsam, *Thomas Chippendale*, 1951 (132).

PROV: Bought by Stephen Winkworth during the 1920s from 'Mr Kerridge, a cabinet maker of genius'; Sotheby's, 28 April 1933, lot 750; G. W. Wrangham, Leathley Hall, Yorkshire; bought with the aid of a government grant 1938.   [23/38]

DESKS
Davenports

240 PORTABLE DESK
*c.*1730
Oak; pine, beech

In the form of a box with a sloping front opening on to loper supports, the exterior and inner surfaces japanned with chinoiserie scenes in gold and silver on a red ground. The interior is fitted with five drawers arranged in two rows centering on pigeonholes and the shaped base drawer containing internal partitions is stained red; brass lifting handles, escutcheons and knobs. The hinged flap is decorated with a cavalry combat while the ends, top, and inner surfaces are japanned with Chinese figures in garden landscapes with oriental buildings, trees, birds and insects. Pine carcase, oak drawer linings, the lopers and blocked drawer fronts beech.
H.20 (8); W.39 (15½); D.26 (10½).

PROV: The Gascoigne gift 1971.   [23.21/71]

240

castors.
H.79 (31); W.62 (24½); D.62 (24½).

The door lock is impressed 'J. T. NEEDS / 100 NEW BOND ST / LATE J. BRAMAH / 124 PICCADILLY'; the fall-front lock is stamped 'S. MORDAN & Co / LONDON / PATENT' and the writing flap hinges are inscribed 'G & W / PATENT NO 1'. J. T. Needs are recorded at this address in *Trade Directories* from 1888 to 1901, S. Mordan & Co. occur throughout the period.

PROV: Formerly owned by Florence Nightingale, Waverley Abbey, Surrey; given to Gwendolen Gascoigne and inherited by her son Sir Alvary; the Gascoigne gift 1968.

[7.156/68]

242 LADY'S DESK
*c.*1900
Sycamore; mahogany, cedar, satinwood, pine

241 DAVENPORT
*c.*1895
Walnut; burr maple, bird's-eye maple, mahogany, cedar

The square flat top veneered with burr maple is surrounded by a low gallery on three sides and fitted behind the fall-front frieze with a desk drawer equipped with a sloping leather-covered writing flap, small drawers, a pen-tray and various compartments lined throughout in bird's-eye maple tipped with rosewood fillets. The table is supported on a central pedestal, the sides panelled in figured walnut and the ends faced with a carved openwork design of interlaced ribbons backed by red silk; the left-hand end contains a tier of four narrow mahogany-fronted drawers with cedar linings and decorative ormolu handles, enclosed by a door. The pedestal, styled with channelled pilasters and carved corbels, is mounted on base runners ending in scrolls hollowed for

241

242

The hinged, sloping top is decorated with an oval chequered string surrounded by a beaded pattern in satinwood with ivory centres and a similar outer border; the four sides are outlined with banding and strings and there is a small drawer below the desk; raised on square tapered legs; the interior is fitted with a velvet-panelled writing flap backed by bottle-wells and a pen-tray; brass locks and gilt ring handles. Mahogany carcase veneered with harewood and inset with ebony, box and satinwood; the desk lined with cedar, pine drawer bottom.
H.81 (32); W.43 (17); D.33 (13).

Although small desks raised on legs were fashionable in the first half of the eighteenth century they were superseded during the last half by neatly fitted writing boxes designed to rest on a table. This example reflects the Sheraton revival and is not based on period prototypes.

PROV: Given by Frank H. Fulford 1939.   [9.52/39]

243 ROLL-TOP DESK
By C. Alstrom, London
c.1905
Mahogany; oak, pine, cedar

Of rectangular kneehole design with a panelled back, ends and sides; each pedestal contains four graduated drawers headed by a document slide. The writing bed is backed by a tier of pigeonholes, small drawers and pockets. An automatic locking action operates on all drawers when the roll-top is closed. Pine and oak carcase, cedar drawers, brass handles.
H.96 (38); W.137 (54); D.75 (29½).

The lock plate is inscribed 'Britism Desk ENGLISH MAKE' – the trade mark of C. Alstrom, 74 and 76, Great Eastern Street, London, wholesale cabinet makers. The kneehole drawer contains an ivoret label 'WM RICHARD-SON (FURNISHERS) LTD / HOME AND OFFICE / FURNISHERS / LEEDS & BRADFORD' while the under-side bears a printed paper label 'WM RICHARDSON (Furnishers), LTD., / CABINET MAKERS AND UP-HOLSTERERS, / 7 & 12 PARK LANE / LEEDS' numbered in ink '67024'.

PROV: Colonel F. R. T. Gascoigne, Lotherton Hall; the Gascoigne gift 1971.   [23.2/71]

DUMB-WAITER

244 DUMB-WAITER
Early 20th century
Mahogany

The central turned column, set on a plain tripod with claw and ball feet, supports a diminishing tier of three circular revolving trays with bead and billet rims. The stem sections are screwed together and when dismantled the trays can be detached.
H.86 (34); Diam. 51 (20).

The thin timber, weak design and lack of wear leave no doubt that this is a reproduction piece.

PROV: Given by Colonel and Mrs J. Hobbins 1956.
          [19.3/56]

GLOBE-STAND

245 PAIR OF TERRESTRIAL AND CELESTIAL GLOBES
c.1760–70
By John Bennett, London
Oak

The horizon circles are raised on four columns with flat cross-stretchers centering on low pillar supports; the bun feet conceal brass castors. Hollow papier-mâché spheres with a plaster shell, the surface details printed on paper divided into gores and tinted red, green and brown and coated in yellow varnish; the brass meridians, marked with degrees, which encircle the orbs and into which the poles of the axis are set permitting rotation, are borne on short pillars and can be tilted to raise or depress the poles; the upper end of each axis is fitted with an hour circle and pointer, the horizon circles are overlaid with paper on which is printed a per-petual calendar showing days of the month; periods indi-cating the sun's place in the Zodiac; points of the compass, fixed feasts and winds.
H.127 (50); Diam. of globes 71 (28).

During restoration of the celestial globe undertaken in 1972 it was possible to look inside the orb. The fabric of the globe – made in two halves – is supported on a six-arm ash spider, the arms being turned with blocked ends. The inner wall is lined with scrap paper – fragments of manuscript, printed matter and torn gores; the next layer is brown papier-mâché approximately $\frac{3}{16}$ in. thick, then an outer layer of white plaster about $\frac{1}{4}$ in. thick; the printed paper gores are stuck to the plaster surface. The sphere is balanced by attaching canvas bags, each containing 1 lb. 12 oz. of lead shot to the inside of the globe.

The terrestrial orb is inscribed 'GLOBUS / TERR-AQUEUS / omnes Regiones hactenus / exploratas exhibens, secundum / nuperas Observationes Astronomicas / et Navigantium ac Itinerantium / fide digniorum relationes consectus / Opera Johan Senex / R.S.S.' and the maker's label is pasted immediately below 'Sold by J. Bennett Instrument Maker at the Globe / in Crown Court St Ann's Soho LONDON'.

The celestial orb carries two inscriptions in English and Latin, the former reads 'The / CELESTIAL GLOBE / On

which the True Face of the Heavens is delineated, & / the Constellations containing upwards of 2000 Stars more / than are on any former Globes, are laid down from / the most recent & Accurate / Observations of Astronomers / and Adjusted to the Year 1740 / By JON: SENEX FRS / Now made & sold with Several New Improvements by / BENJ: MARTIN only, in Fleet Street London 1757'.

John Bennett evidently acquired the globes themselves from Benjamin Martin who succeeded John Senex (d.1740) as publisher of the famous Senex globes. Bennett flourished *c.*1745–70 at the Globe, Crown Court, Soho; he is described in *Kent's Directory* as a mathematical instrument maker and, since it was customary practice at the time, would certainly have supplied the pillared stands. His trade card is reproduced by H. R. Calvert, *Scientific Trade Cards in the Science Museum Collection*, 1971, pl.9. In 1758 Benjamin Martin advertised a pair of 28 inch Senex Globes made with 'exquisite skill, taste and elegance' in carved mahogany frames and silvered meridians at £35.

LIT: *Furniture History*, III (1967) p.20.

EXH: *Temple Newsam Heirlooms*, 1972 (30).

PROV: These globes are recorded in the Temple Newsam inventory of 1808 'Library, 11th Room 1st Floor – 2 very large 28 Inch Globes in wainscot frames with green serge covers'; given by the Earl of Halifax 1922.   [1922/F.24]

246

KNIFE CASES

246 BOX KNIFE CASE
*c.*1785
Mahogany; tulipwood, box, ebony, pine

In the form of a box with a sloping lid and elaborately shaped front; the pine carcase is veneered in mahogany, crossbanded with tulipwood and the corners are outlined by obliquely chequered strings; the interior of the lid is inset with an eight-pointed star executed in boxwood and ebony while the inner face, cut with 52 slots for knives, forks and spoons, is intersected by a grid of chequered lines with pine partitions below; raised on low feet. The silver lock escutcheon, devised as a shield suspended from tied ribbons, is engraved with an heraldic crest of a wyvern holding an arrow in its mouth; oval handle escutcheon missing, brass lock and hinges.
H.38 (15); W.23 (9); D.27 (10½).

Probably originally one of a pair.

PROV: The crest belongs to the Jenkins family; given by Colonel and Mrs J. Hobbins 1956.   [9.2/56]

247 PAIR OF BOX KNIFE CASES
Late 18th century
Mahogany; pine

In the form of boxes with sloping lids and shaped blockfronts enriched with chequered corner strings; the lids are decorated inside with ebony and boxwood stars while each internal face, slotted to take 37 knives, forks and spoons, is outlined with a grid of strings. Mounted with oval silver escutcheons enhanced by bright-cut engraving. Pine carcase and inner partitions, brass locks and oval hinges.
H.36 (14¼); W.23 (9); D.26 (10¼).

PROV: Agnes and Norman Lupton Bequest 1953.
    [13.388/53]

248 PAIR OF VASE KNIFE CASES
*c.*1795
Satinwood; birch, tulipwood, mahogany, pine, ebony, box

The vase, raised on a low circular foot, stands on a square

248

LECTERNS

LECTERN, iron and leather
Designed by C. E. Kempe, 1877
Under Cat. No.533 (illustrated)

249 LECTERN
By Joubert
*c.*1910
Gilt beech; pine

Of framed-X construction supporting a plain pine board.
The taller uprights are styled as pilasters decorated with
panels of foliate strapwork, scale ornament and Ionic scrolls;
the shorter posts are elaborately turned and carved with
acanthus bands, fluting and gadrooned knops. The two X
supports are connected by a turned central bar and carved
stretcher rails.
H.152 (60); W.86 (34).

base inlaid with chequered strings and a 'Van Dyke' border;
the sides and domed cover segmented with herringbone
strings in light, dark and green-stained woods; turned acorn
finial. The lid is raised on a square mahogany rod sliding in a
central tube, being held up by steel springs; the lower stage
provides a circular stepped platform slotted to accommodate
21 knives, 18 forks and 12 spoons; the interior partitioned by
three concentric shells of coopered pine. Old pin-holes
indicate that the late Victorian silver escutcheon embossed
with naturalistic ornament replaces an earlier mount; the
base is lined with maroon leather. The stem, dome cover and
carcase turned birch, the sheer sides and mahogany plinth
veneered with satinwood, the stepped platform veneered in
tulipwood on a mahogany foundation with box rings and an
outer border of ebony, the central rod and tube mahogany
cased in box, internal structures pine.
H. closed 62 (24½); Diam. 28 (11).

Hepplewhite observed that vase knife cases 'are usually
made of satin or other light-coloured wood, and may be
placed at each end on the sideboards'. Sheraton provides
contemporary evidence that they were made by specialist
firms (*Drawing-Book*, p.392). Knife cases of closely similar
design are illustrated in *D.E.F.*, II, p.276, fig.9 and by M.
Jourdain and F. Rose, *Georgian Furniture*, 1953, pl.159.

LIT: *L.A.C.*, No.32–3 (1956), p.27, repr.

PROV: John Ambler, Killinghall, Yorkshire whose father had
   bought them prior to 1914; given by Lady Martin through
   the L.A.C.F. 1955.   [20.2/55]

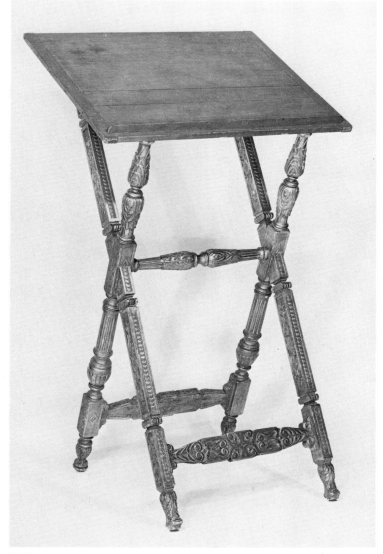

249

The lectern was commissioned by Colonel F. R. T. Gascoigne for the York Missal, *c*.1400, now on permanent loan to York Minster. Executed by Joubert, a French decorator working in London who, in addition to crafting this florid Italianate baroque style bookrest, made items of reproduction 'lion's-mask' furniture formerly at Lotherton and supplied the wrought iron gates and sundial in the garden between *c*.1905–12.

PROV: Recorded in the 1930s Lotherton inventory 'Gilt Bookstand – Made by Joubert for the York Missal'; the Gascoigne gift 1968. [7.182/68]

LIBRARY STEPS

250 LIBRARY POLE-LADDER
Late 18th century
Mahogany

Built of two D-section uprights with the inner faces grooved centrally; the hinged rungs have brass ferrules and are designed to fold into the slots by pressing one side up and inward towards the other; when extended two iron stays keep the sides braced, when closed the two halves become an oval pole united by six hook-and-eye fitments. Lower rung renewed.
Extended: H.241 (95); W.39 (15½).
Closed: H.274 (108); Diam. 3½ × 2½ in.

Plate xxii in Ince and Mayhew's *Universal System of Household Furniture* (1759–62) illustrates a design for library steps contrived to fold on the same principle. The relevant note implies they were considered suitable for small rooms. There is a closely similar pole-ladder at Crowe Hall, Bath and another at Corsham Court with a brass locking device to unite the uprights impressed 'TAYLORS / PATENT'. A third example is illustrated in E. Pinto, *Treen*, 1969, pl.271.

LIT: *Furniture History*, III (1967) p.16 and 26.

EXH: *Temple Newsam Heirlooms*, 1972 (32).

PROV: This item is recorded in the Temple Newsam inventory of 1808 (Y.A.S. Library DD.54) 'Library, 11th Room 1st Floor – A pair of folding library steps'; bought at the Temple Newsam sale (Robinson, Fisher & Harding), 26–31 July 1922, lot 217. [1922/F.17]

250

LINEN PRESSES

251 LINEN PRESS
Probably late 18th century
Mahogany

The base board, raised on low runners, supports two spiral threaded uprights which pass loosely through holes in the cross-battened upper plate, pressure being applied by means of circular nuts with cross-bar handles.
H.17·8 (7); W.44 (17½); D.28 (11).

EXH: *Temple Newsam Heirlooms*, 1972 (34).

PROV: The Ingrams of Temple Newsam; given by the Earl of Halifax 1922. [1922/F30]

252

251

252 LINEN PRESS
Early 19th century
Mahogany; oak, pine

The rectangular box base, fitted with a drawer, has an upright post at each end connected by a head rail; a central batten on the upper leaf supports a large wooden screw threaded through the head rail, pressure being applied by turning a cross-bar handle. Styled with corner mouldings; the drawer is outlined by a boxwood string; turned feet missing. Mahogany, with an oak drawer and pine bottom.
H.56 (22); W.38 (15); D.30·5 (12).

The underside of the drawer is stencilled '9475' and bears a printed label 'GEORGE DOBSON & SON, / Furniture Dealers, / AND LICENSED VALUERS, / 33, COOK-RIDGE STREET, LEEDS / ESTAB 1866'. In 1901 George Dobson & Son moved from 18, Park Row to 33, Cookridge Street where they remained until the firm closed in 1927.

PROV: Agnes and Norman Lupton Bequest 1953 [13.503/53]

LOOKING-GLASSES

253 LOOKING-GLASS
*c.*1720
Gilt pine

Of rectangular design with slightly shaped, rounded corners; the bevelled plate is contained in a narrow moulded surround headed by an arched, backward-curving crest styled with scrolling acanthus fronds on a punched ground and a central scallop shell. Marks under the lower rail show where the original candlearms were attached.
H.99 (39); W.61 (24).

PROV: Frank Savery; bought 1953. [15.5/53]

254 LOOKING-GLASS
*c.*1725
Gilt pine

The rectangular bevelled plate, contained in a moulded border enriched with leafy strapwork, is headed by a winged cherub-mask surmounted by three tall plumes; the open

cresting with gadrooned horns and fronded corner scrolls is lightly patterned with foliate strapwork and husk motifs; the elaborately shaped and similarly styled base centres on a *lambrequin* fan between two leaf-cup brackets drilled to receive candlearms.
H.132 (52); W.74 (29).

PROV: Agnes and Norman Lupton Bequest 1952.   [5.522/52]

253

255 LOOKING-GLASS
*c.*1728–30
Gilt pine

The rectangular mirror plate, bordered by a narrow gadrooned moulding, is surmounted by an elaborately shaped cresting enriched with acanthus fronds on a punched ground and centering on a satyr-mask headed by a scallop fan detailed with shells and husks; the shoulders are styled with volutes, while the lower corner scrolls bear blanks for fixing on candlearms (decorated at a later date with composition shells); the shaped base is embellished with a formal shell between fronds. Modern glass.

254

H.112 (44); W.56 (22).

PROV: Agnes and Norman Lupton bequest 1952.   [5.521/52]

256 LOOKING-GLASS
*c.*1725–30
Gilt pine

The plate, set in a rectangular frame with squared corner lugs, is bordered by an inner bead-and-reel and outer leaf moulding divided by a trail of foliage with florets at each corner; the straight broken pediment centres on a ribbed shell and the tympanum is enriched with crossed acanthus sprays on a punched ground; the shaped base, styled with fronds and a fluted shell, has scroll corners designed for attaching candlearms. Each side is set with two staples, possibly intended for a strut to brace the hinged arms.
H.86 (34); W.59 (23½).

The backboard bears remnants of a mid nineteenth century newspaper and the trade label of J. A. Lewis & Son,

Brompton Road, London.

PROV: J. A. Lewis & Son; Frank Savery; bought 1953.

[15.2/53]

255

256

H.117 (46); W.75 (29½).

PROV: Bequeathed by Frank Savery 1966.   [1.1/66]

257 LOOKING-GLASS
c.1730–35
Gilt pine

The rectangular bevelled plate is contained in a moulded border tooled with a design of foliate strapwork and florets in low relief; the open scrolled cresting with fronded corners and acanthus spray volutes is centred by a leafy cartouche featuring a husk motif; the shoulders and elaborately shaped base, ornamented with a scallop shell, are tooled with naturalistic floral sprays; the gesso surface is textured with circular stamps and burnished details. The glass plate replaced.

258 LOOKING-GLASS
c.1730–35
Walnut; pine

The rectangular glass is bordered by a veneered walnut frame with gilt enriched inner and outer mouldings; the pedimented cresting of scroll design with acanthus volutes centres on a baroque cartouche; the straight sides support leafy flower and fruit pendants; elaborately lobed base.
H.129 (51); W.69 (27).

PROV: Bequeathed by Frank Savery 1966.   [1.2/66]

257

259 LOOKING-GLASS

*c.*1735
Walnut; pine

The rectangular frame has narrow carved and gilt acanthus mouldings, a shaped base and a swan-neck pediment terminating in frond volutes with a cartouche in the embrasure bearing a leaf rosette in low relief, the sides are edged with festoons of fringed drapery. Two circular patches and nail holes on the frieze suggest that a central carved and gilt applied ornament is missing which may have been matched by another motif on the base. Pine frame and backboard; veneered with figured walnut, the mouldings and salient ornaments in gilt pine, the gesso enriched with stamps. Inscribed on the back in pencil 'Rose Dressing Rm'.
H.132 (52); W.67 (26½).

This mirror is similar in many respects to one from Hedingham Castle, Essex, illustrated in *D.E.F.*, II, p.336, pl.64.

PROV: St Clement Dane's Vicarage, London; Frank Savery; bought 1953.   [5.1/53]

258

260 PAIR OF PIER GLASSES

*c.*1735–40
Gilt pine

The rectangular bevelled plates are set in gilt frames of architectural design enriched with egg and dart mouldings, sand-textured and stamped surfaces; the broken pediments centre on a cartouche with fronded scrolls bearing a leaf-drop and the friezes are richly ornamented with shells and arabesques; the sides are edged with oak pendants and the pierced apron is styled with a formalized shell and frond carving in low relief.
H.175 (69); W.84 (33).

PROV: By descent to the Earl of Halifax, Hickleton Hall, Yorkshire; Hickleton Hall sale (Hollis & Webb, Leeds) 18–22 March 1947, lots 306 & 307, pl. viii; W. Foster; bought from Armour Trust, Ltd 1949.   [12/49]

262 LOOKING-GLASS

*c.*1740
Mahogany; pine

The rectangular frame has variously carved and gilt mouldings, a shaped base and a swan-neck pediment terminating
in small shells and centering on a scrolled cartouche figuring

259

261 LOOKING-GLASS

*c.*1740
Walnut, pine

The rectangular bevelled plate is contained within a veneered
walnut frame bordered with gilt acanthus mouldings; the
scrolled cresting with fronded rosette volutes centres on a
foliate cartouche featuring a lion's head erased on a torse;
elaborately shaped base.
H.129 (51); W.69 (27).

The heraldic crest is not an original feature

PROV: W. F. Greenwood & Son, York; Digby Chamberlain;
given by Mrs H. Garrett 1967.   [18/67]

260

a leaf-drop; the sides are edged with oak leaf and acorn pendants, the frieze is ornamented with stylized acanthus foliage and the corners with small frond motifs. Pine frame and backboard, veneered with mahogany, the mouldings and applied ornaments in gilt pine, the gesso enriched with circular stamps. The composition shells replace original fronded rosettes.

H.155 (61); W.76 (30).

PROV: Alfred Jowett; bought 1954. [12.2/54]

261

262

263 LOOKING-GLASS
*c.*1745 (perhaps 1876)
Walnut; pine

The shoulders and cresting are of scrolled profile design with incised and gilt sprays below a central eagle perched on a stunted tree; leafy fruit and flower side pendants; the shaped base is incised with gilt foliage and the wave-pattern inner border has a gilt enriched moulding. Pine frame veneered in walnut.

H.112 (44); W.60 (23½).

The silvered mirror plate bears a rubber stamp 'AG / MAR / 1876 / LONDON' within a lozenge. The backboard showed no evidence of having been removed before which suggests this looking glass may belong to the Chippendale Revival period. Firms such as Samuel Hassall of Halifax and Thomas Ferrand of York are known to have been producing mirrors of a similar pattern during early Victorian days.

PROV: Bought from Frank Savery 1953. [15.3/53]

263

264 LOOKING-GLASS
*c.*1745–50
Gilt pine

264

The shaped plate is set within a frame composed of long scrolls flanked by floral festoons and palm branches with a frilled inner border; a female head crowned with leaves springs from each shoulder; the cresting, ornamented with a rococo shell formation between acanthus sprays, supports a tall frond and the base centres on a circular cartouche linked to the corner scrolls by a mirror border; richly tooled and textured surface.
H.236 (93); W.137 (54).

PROV: Bought from Montague Marcussen (Antiques) 1944.
[21/44]

265 PIER GLASS
*c.*1750–55
Attributed to Matthias Lock, London
Gilt pine

The shaped cresting centres on a female bust crowned by a tall acanthus plume set between crossed boughs and floral sprays; the upper shoulders are decorated with long-necked birds perched on spiralling vine stems; the lower plate is

265

265

contained within a moulded frame supporting floral trails headed by winged female terms attired in fronded crowns, floral girdles and leafy skirts; the serpentine lower rail centres on an open-mouthed rococo mask between scrolling acanthus foliage with floral swags and flame aprons below; the uprights terminate in low plinths and the junction of the two mirror plates is concealed by twin oak branches. H.318 (125); W.142 (56).

The frame members are screwed on to a flat backboard which supports the mirror plate. The looking-glass was evidently imported from France since it is lightly engraved '? Menbrs / Julliet 157'.

The flamboyant design displays, in its combination of female heads, exotic birds, vine spirals, rococo masks and floral garlands, interesting analogies with drawings by Matthias Lock in the V. & A. Compare for example a design (Lock Album, No.54), published in *A New Book of Ornament* by M. Lock and H. Copland, 1752, pl. i. This engraving cannot be regarded as a source for the frame, but

the system of decorative elements and festive styling suggest he supplied the design for this mirror.

LIT: *Apollo*, April 1942, p.86, repr.; *Antiques*, Sept. 1968, p.360, repr.; A. Coleridge, *Chippendale Furniture*, 1968, pl.98.

PROV: H.R.H. The Duke of Kent; Frank Partridge & Sons; given by Lady Martin 1942. [16/42]

266

266 PIER GLASS
*c.*1755–60
Stripped pine, formerly painted

Elaborately shaped frame designed with glass borders, the outer surround composed of long fronded scrolls ornamented with pendant fruit and flowers, rising to ogee-crested shoulders surmounted by a large basket of fruit and three native birds; the upper plate centres on a wreath suspended from tied ribbons and the lower plate is contained within faceted columns and C-scrolls; the base, richly carved with laurel swags, acanthus sprays and rockwork corners, incorporates shell formations and falling water; the whole system is styled with volutes, garlands, flame borders, spiky foliage and rococo fringes. Traces of the original white finish visible, some peripheral carving missing.
H.251 (99); W.114 (45).

PROV: Bought from Rice & Christy, Ltd 1945.   [14.1/45]

267

267 LOOKING-GLASS
*c.*1755–60
Gilt pine

The shaped inner surround bordered with flamework and ribbed bands is festooned with open leafy fruit and flower side pendants; the pierced cresting is composed of a system of foliate scrolls supporting a basket of flowers and the base is similarly styled with ribbed and fronded C-scrolls centering on a carved spray.
H.112 (44); W.66 (26).

PROV: Frank Savery; bought 1953.   [15.4/53]

268 LOOKING-GLASS
*c.*1760
Gilt lime

The oval mirror plate is framed by a vigorously carved and gilt flame cartouche ornamented with gothic frets, incised diaper patterns, C-scrolls and a fantastic outer system of rococo foliage, falling water, flowers and scrolled brackets supporting rockwork compositions and, on the shoulders, a pair of Chinese ho-ho birds; the base is decorated with a small asymmetrical cartouche and the elaborately styled cresting centres on a fanciful grotto, featuring water issuing from beneath a rococo shell with a winged female dragon above.
H.249 (96); W.142 (56).

The broad flame borders combined with spiky foliage, exotic birds, dragons, rockwork, falling water and diverse rococo elements are stylistically related to plates in Thomas Johnson's *Collection of Designs*, 1758, although the parallels hardly justify an attribution to this craftsman.

LIT: *L.A.C.*, No.32–3 (1956), p.31, repr.; A. Coleridge, *Chippendale Furniture*, 1968, pl.111.

PROV: Captain Fenwick, Brinkburn Priory, Northumberland; Brinkburn Priory sale (Sanderson, Townend & Gilbert, Newcastle-upon-Tyne) 18–20 July 1955, lot 278; William Young Ltd; bought 1956.   [6/56]

269 PIER GLASS
*c.*1760
Gilt pine

The glass is in three sections with moulded border panels and a shaped top plate cut with a dove holding an olive branch (symbolising Peace); the elaborately pierced and gilt outer frame, carved with flowing scrolls, clusters of fruit, garlands, palm leaves and rococo foliage, rises to a scrolled cresting of flamboyant rococo design; the narrower inner frame features clustered columns on a rockwork base with tiers of faceted columns above headed by leaf capitals; the central plate has a shaped rococo surround with flame fringes

concealing joins in the glass and a floral spray arranged across the moulded arch.
H.272 (107); W.140 (55).

The mirror plate clearly dates from about 1710 when narrow frames and shaped crestings which emphasized the richly moulded borders were fashionable. It was evidently reset in the present lavishly ornamented frame some fifty years later. The practice of re-using looking-glass plates was quite common in the eighteenth century owing to their heavy cost and it is likely that, to reduce the risk of breakage, this mirror was reframed by a local York firm.

A photograph of the mirror *in situ* at Howsham shows lateral pendants of fruit and flowers falling from the angular shoulders to a point level with the base.

EXH: Temple Newsam, *Thomas Chippendale*, 1951 (128).

PROV: By descent from Nathaniel Cholmley of Howsham Hall, Yorkshire to the Hon. Mrs I. M. H. Strickland; Howsham Hall sale (Hollis & Webb, Leeds) 1–4 Nov 1948, lot 323, pl.iv; given by Lady Martin 1948.   [27/48]

269

270 LOOKING-GLASS

*c.*1760
Papier-mâché; pine

The rectangular glass plate with decorative bevelled borders and a leaf spray motif cut in the spandrels is of early eighteenth century date, slightly reduced at the top, and set in a mid eighteenth century white painted and gilt *en carton* frame. The gadrooned outer surround and the inner flame-work border, headed by a shaped cresting, are of pine faced with papier-mâché enrichments. The sides are elaborately ornamented with a system of open fronded scrolls, leafy twigs and floral festoons incorporating urns and columns, modelled in papier-mâché and inhabited by putti playing

270

musical instruments, squirrels eating nuts, and birds. The top is surmounted by an eagle gripping a feathered scroll between boughs; leafy branches at the base originally centered on a pair of dancing putti. The main mirror plate is in two sections divided by a floral swag with a separate head-plate and borders; pine backboard. The frame was originally entirely gilt.
H.249 (98); W.183 (72).

The papier-mâché reliefs are composed of layered paper, the hollow interior backed by cardboard, with a wire inserted into some delicate elements. The production of papier-mâché mirror frames in mid Georgian London is discussed by G. Wills, *English Looking-Glasses*, 1965, pp.138–42, but no design source or maker has been identified in this instance. The gallery at Doddington Hall, Lincs, is decorated with an impressive array of gilt papier-mâché mirror frames and mural ornaments; the latter are strikingly similar to those surrounding this frame, which suggests they too may survive from a unified wall scheme.

PROV: By descent from Sir William Strickland, 4th Bart. of Boynton, Yorkshire to the Rev. J. E. Strickland; purchased at the Boynton Hall sale (Henry Spencer, Retford) 21–23 Nov. 1950, lot 124 (illustrated).   [42.3/50]

271

271 PAIR OF PIER GLASSES
*c.*1760
Gilt pine

Rectangular, bevelled plates set in elaborately carved and gilt frames; the shaped inner borders have a flame surround with pierced and incised enrichment; the sides ornamented with scrolling foliage, small brackets and other rococo elements, rise to an openwork cresting featuring a fanciful Chinese pagoda supported by four columns resting on a rockwork platform, the base is styled with C-scrolls centering on a foliate motif. The plates have been re-silvered and the frames re-gilded.
H.168 (66); W.85 (33½).

Francis Bamford, the acknowledged authority on Scottish furniture, is confident these looking-glasses were made in

Edinburgh; they are similar in many respects to a pair at Brechin Castle, Angus.

LIT: *L.A.C.*, No.14 (1950), p.6, repr.; *Antiques*, May 1970, p.723, fig.13.

PROV: By descent from Duncan Forbes of Balgownie House, Old Aberdeen (taken to Rothiemay Castle, Banffshire in 1896) to Colonel Ian Forbes; uncatalogued sale (Robert Downie, Aberdeen) Sept. 1948; William Young, Ltd; bought 1950.   [22/50]

272 PIER GLASS
*c.*1760–65
Gilt pine

The oval plate contained in a moulded frame carved with shellwork at the top, is surrounded by an open system of fronded rococo scrolls crested by an acanthus plume; the shoulders are decorated with falling water, the sides incorporate floral festoons and the base centres on figures of a sheep and goat posed on a rocky mound framed by C-scrolls.
H.112 (44); W.65 (25½).

The sheep and goat motif is copied (in reverse) from a mirror design in Thomas Johnson's *A New Book of Ornaments*,

272

1760, pl.2. An identical mirror, apparently the pair to this example, is illustrated by G. Wills, *English Looking-Glasses*, 1965, fig.103. Several sheets of paper were found between the backboard and the glass plate; one, perhaps dating from the Georgian period, bears a scribble sketch and a sum amounting to £2.4.4, a later piece of brown paper is inscribed (twice) 'Mrs Steele, Valley Drive'.

EXH: Temple Newsam, *L.A.C.F. Members Exhibition*, 1952 (254).

PROV: Claude Norton, Scarborough; bequeathed by Sir George Martin 1976.   [51.13/76]

PAIR OF PIER GLASSES, painted and gilt
By Vile and Cobb, London, 1761
Under Cat. No.452 (illustrated here and frontispiece Vol 2)

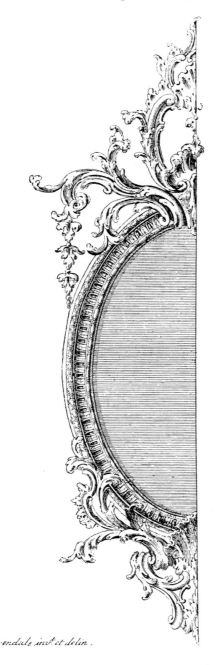

452

273 LOOKING-GLASS
*c.*1765
Gilt pine

The rectangular glass is framed by an enriched moulding, the sides are surrounded by pierced flame borders and the cresting and base are formed of a matching system of open C-scrolls combined with rococo foliage. The carved work is reinforced behind with narrow wooden spines.
H.86 (34); W.53 (22).

The backboard is inscribed in pencil 'R & G New Glass Dec 96' and the mirror plate is padded with a newspaper of 1896. The frame probably contained a painting at some time.

PROV: Agnes and Norman Lupton Bequest 1952. [5.523/52]

274 LOOKING-GLASS
*c.*1770
Mahogany; pine

274

The rectangular plate, bordered by a gilt enriched moulding, is contained in a veneered mahogany frame styled with pierced carved and gilt fruit, flower and leaf pendants at each side, a shaped base and scrolling ears at each corner; the open cresting is ornamented with gilt foliated scrolls centering on an urn and flower spray.
H.123 (48½); W.56 (22).

PROV: David Dunstan Schofield Bequest 1962.   [18.29/62]

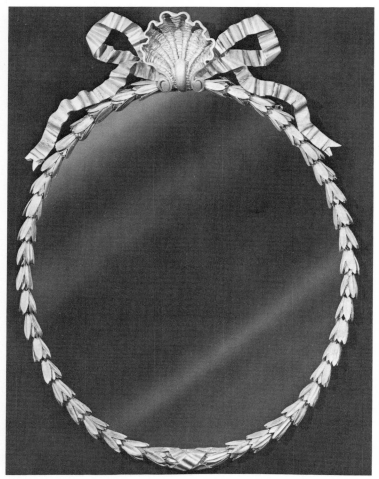

275

275 PIER GLASS
c.1774
Gilt pine

Oval mirror plate with carved and gilt husk chain surround; the cresting is in the form of a large crimped shell backed by a tied ribbon and with crossed ribbons at the base. New glass and back panel.
H.129 (51); W.94 (37).

Formerly one of a pair, the companion is now owned by A.M.G. Galliers-Pratt of Mawley Hall. Possibly designed by Sir William Chambers who worked at Newburgh Priory and at Lord Fauconberg's London house in 1774. The French classicism of this design is certainly consistent with his

authorship; it also displays affinities with his architectural ornament.

PROV: By descent from the Earls of Fauconberg to Captain V. M. Wombwell of Newburgh Priory, Yorkshire; bought 1946.   [19.1/46]

276 PAIR OF PIER GLASSES
c.1775
Gilt pine

Rectangular gilt frames flanked by long consoles with scrolled foliate bases; the outer surrounds enriched with waterleaf, the inner borders are reeded with a ribbon twist. The tops have square corner lugs containing circular paterae with husk chain pendants punctuated by tied ribbons which mask joints in the glass borders. The open scrolled crestings are ornamented with husk festoons and incorporate standing figures of a cow and a charging bull; the lower borders display three classical urns. The mirror plates are in two sections, the join being concealed by a string of husks.
H.259 (102); W.140 (55).

It is apparent that the open scroll crestings were originally surmounted by an ornamental feature – possibly a classical urn relating to those in the lower border. The charging bull motif was used occasionally by neo-classical designers; it features prominently on a marquetry commode at the Lady Lever Art Gallery (Macquoid, *Catalogue*, III, no.329) but the presence of a companion cow is certainly unusual.

PROV: By descent from the Earls of Lindsey of Uffington House, Lincolnshire to Lady Muriel Barclay-Harvey (having been rescued from the great fire at Uffington in 1904); bought 1953.   [12.2/53]

277 LOOKING-GLASS
c.1775–80
Gilt pine and composition

Rectangular frame with inner and outer husk chain surrounds forming a wide border on three sides backed by mirror plates; the side panels contain a symmetrical design of fronded scrolls alternating with draped rams'-heads and half-round brackets incorporating brass sockets for candle branches; the upper border is decorated with anthemion and husk rings centering on a garlanded bucranium masking a seventh socket. The frame and principal ornaments carved and gilt pine, the applied arabesque and secondary husk chain motifs are in gilt composition with a wire core. Original glass, the central plate re-silvered, local restoration in upper border.
H.244 (88); W.127 (50).

PROV: The Earl of Portsmouth; Kelso Ltd; given by Frank H. Fulford 1939.   [9.46/39]

276

277

278 LOOKING-GLASS
Early 19th century
Gilt pine

The circular concave glass, set in an ebonized reeded slip surround, is contained in a gilt cavetto outer frame studded with balls and bordered by a waterleaf moulding. Slots cut into the back indicate where carved cresting and base ornaments were fixed and screw holes at each side show that it once supported candlearms.
Diam: 46 (18).

PROV: Agnes and Norman Lupton Bequest 1952. [5.524/52]

279 PIER GLASS
c.1830
Pine; oak, composition

Rectangular mirror plate in two sections framed between pilasters with raised borders styled as colonettes with leaf bases and capitals, the panels headed by floral pendants; plain architrave surmounted by a lotus moulding and an elaborately shaped open cresting enriched with composition ornament in the rococo taste centering on a cabochon cartouche below a small platform; the composition decoration is applied to a painted tympanum embellished with gilt chinoiserie birds. Green painted and gilt pine frame with oak bottom rail.
H.302 (119); 173 (68).

This pier glass is an integral feature of the Chinese Drawing Room at Temple Newsam which was remodelled by Lady Hertford c.1828–30. Many of the fittings evidently came from a French château of the Louis XIV period and this mirror with its flamboyant cresting inhabited by exotic birds and gaudy applied decoration contributes to the festive decor. Although the frame has been altered and the cresting added later the piece is an interesting example of the pre Victorian taste for 'made-up' period furniture.

LIT: C. G. Gilbert, 'Lady Hertford, John James Audubon and the Chinese Drawing Room at Temple Newsam', *L.A.C.*, No.61 (1968), pp.14–17.

PROV: By descent from Lady Hertford of Temple Newsam to the Earl of Halifax who gave it to Leeds 1922.

[1922/F22]

280 LOOKING-GLASS
By Newton Bros, Leeds
c.1865
Pine; composition

The rectangular glass is contained in a heavy moulded frame, the concave inner face banded with fluting between coin-pattern and lotus borders executed in composition; the back edge is outlined by a twisted ribbon and the corners are enriched with acanthus fronds. Originally gilt, now grained to simulate rosewood.
H.99 (39); W.86 (34).

The top rail bears a printed paper label inscribed 'Newton Brothers, / Carvers, Gilders & General Decorators, / 58, Park Lane, / Leeds'. The firm is recorded at this address in

280

279

local Directories between 1863 and 1867. According to an entry in *Industries of Yorkshire*, 1888, the business was founded in 1830 by George Newton, father of the then proprietors James and John Newton who were 'decorators, paper hangers, picture-frame makers, gilders, picture cleaners and restorers, and fine art dealers'.

PROV: Temple Newsam; given by the Earl of Halifax 1922.
[1922/F46]

281 LOOKING-GLASS
*c.*1900
Gilt pine

The central mirror is set between two plates bordered by faceted pilasters entwined with stems; the pagoda cresting is flanked by open lattice panels with rockwork and ho-ho birds on the shoulders, the whole elaborately shaped composition being designed in the rococo taste; the side panes are ornamented with falling water at the top and silhouetted Chinese temples at the lower corners; the base of the frame is lavishly carved and pierced with a system of rococo scrolls, fronds, lattice and a flamework arch supporting a small platform; the backboards are of framed panel construction. H.160 (63); W.119 (47).

The design has an interesting ancestry; it was originally published in Matthias Lock's *A New Book of Ornaments for Looking Glass Frames, Chimney Pieces &c* of which only a second edition issued about 1768 survives, but re-strikes of plates from this volume were published in John Weale's curious compendium *A Collection of Ornamental Designs chiefly after Chippendale* printed about 1834 and pl.13 in this collection doubtless provided the immediate source. The rather weak interpretation of the engraved design is not compatible with the vigour of late Regency rococo revival carving, the frame is in fact likely to date from the turn of the last century when reproduction Chippendale-style furniture was in great demand. Charles Erad advertized a very similar 'Large Chippendale Glass' in one of their trade catalogues (Pratt collection, No.178) issued *c*.1905, priced £45.

EXH: Sheffield, Mappin Art Gallery, *Reflections*, 1972 (11).

PROV: Paul Martin Ltd; Christie's, 20 Feb. 1958, lot 95; given by Lady Martin 1958.   [5/58]

281

282 PIER GLASS
*c.*1900
Silvered pine

The bevelled glass is in two sections, the shaped upper plate being cut with a formalized floral pattern and scalloped edge; framed in half-round mouldings enriched with stippled panels of strapwork, husk-drops and leaf rosettes; the high shoulders and scroll cresting carved with acanthus foliage centering on three plumes backed by fronds; silvered surface.
H.180 (71); W.67 (26½).

Formerly one of a pair. A representative specimen of medium quality reproduction gesso furniture; compare Cat. No.401.

PROV: Theda Lady Nussey, Little Rushwood, Sutton Howgrave, Ripon, Yorkshire; sold on the premises (Renton & Renton, Harrogate) 18–19 July, 1962, lot 741; one was bought by Mrs F. D. Marshall, the companion by Sir George Martin who gave his to Leeds 1969.   [13/69]

DRESSING AND TOILET GLASSES

283 TOILET GLASS
*c.*1745
Mahogany; walnut, pine, oak

The serpentine-fronted base, styled with gilt enriched egg and dart and acanthus pattern mouldings, has canted forecorners faced with mirror panels and a long drawer divided by numerous shaped partitions; raised on gilt bracket feet carved with fronds. The standards, capped by gilt pineapples, and the shaped mirror contained within a veneered walnut frame bordered by parcel gilt rococo scrolls, foliage and flamework are not original. Pine base, veneered in mahogany oak mirror frame and backboard, mahogany drawer.
H.80 (31½); W.66 (26); D.28 (11).

EXH: Temple Newsam, *L.A.C.F. Members Exhibition*, 1952 (251); Sheffield, Mappin Art Gallery, *Reflections*, 1972 (8).

PROV: Said to have come from Hampton Court, Herefordshire, but a fragmentary early Victorian advertisement (pasted on to the backboard) issued by John Thornley,

281

283

grocer, at the sign of the Golden Tea Pot, Market Place, Preston, must cast doubt on this provenance; Alfred Jowett; given by Lady Martin 1952. [33/52]

284

284 CHEVAL DRESSING-GLASS
*c.*1770
Mahogany

The upright mirror bordered by a crossbanded surround is suspended between two vertical standards headed by wrythen urn-finials with an intermediate cross rail and lower connecting bar; the moulded uprights are supported on splayed legs richly carved with acanthus foliage, anthemion motifs, rosettes and C-scrolls, the feet conceal brass castors fitted with friction rollers; the shaped cresting is pierced to form a handle; panelled back board. The glass can be raised or lowered by a system of lead weights and sash pulleys contained in the hollow pillars; each weight (15 in. long) is suspended from gut line which travels over a brass wheel set in the finial block.

H.145 (57), raised 180 (71); W.67 (26½).

Sheraton noted in his *Cabinet Dictionary*, p.255, that 'the term "HORSE" is used to denote a kind of tall dressing-glass suspended by two pillars and claws . . . the standards are sometimes glued up hollow to admit a weight on each side equal to the glass and frame, by which means the glass is raised to any height the same as a sash window is'. He illustrates an example in his *Drawing-Book* pl. xvii with further comments on the mechanism.

LIT: *Burlington*, July 1966, p.373, fig.53; *L.A.C.*, No.60 (1967), p.10, fig.4.

PROV: Miss Leonora H. D. Horrocks; Christie's, 20 July 1939, lot 127; J. J. Wolff (Antiques); bequeathed by Frank Savery 1966. [1.3/66]

285 TOILET GLASS
*c.*1795
Mahogany; pine, box, ivory

Shield-shaped glass suspended between curved standards; serpentine-fronted base box with crossbanded borders and

285

corner strings on three sides, raised on low bracket feet. Three mahogany lined drawers with ivory pulls and escutcheon, the standards ornamented with ivory discs. Pine carcase. Originally surmounted by urn finials and a brass eagle.
H.59 (23); W.41 (16½); D.21 (8¼).

The pine backboard inscribed in pencil 'Mr Hodgson / (?) Gonerby' and on the inside 'Glass Wanted', the mirror plate stencilled 'PATENT SILVERING COMPANY'. The new looking-glass was probably inserted by William Hodgson, cut glass manufacturer, who carried on business at 10, Bond Street, Leeds throughout the second half of the nineteenth century.

Shield-shaped dressing glasses were first illustrated in the *London Book of Prices*, 1788, pl.14 and remained fashionable until the Regency period.

PROV: Probably part of the furnishings of Armley House, Leeds, which passed by descent to Mrs Frank Gott of Weetwood Garth; bequeathed 1941. [7.15/41]

286 CHEVAL DRESSING-GLASS
*c.*1800
Mahogany

Simple rectangular frame styled with sunk panels, the splayed legs terminate in square socket castors surmounted by turned finials. The back is decorated with a hand-painted Chinese picture of two court ladies, mounted on canvas.
H.175 (69); W.66 (26).

At this date most cheval glasses were either suspended between two pillars by centre screws or made to rise and fall by weights (Cat. No.284). The back painting is an interesting expression of the Regency taste for chinoiserie and could imply that the piece was commissioned for a 'Chinese' bedroom.

PROV: Agnes and Norman Lupton Bequest 1953.
[13.376/53]

DRESSING TABLE GLASS, mahogany
By Gillows, Lancaster, 1811
Under Cat. No.501 (illustrated)

DRESSING TABLE GLASS, papier-mâché
Birmingham, *c.*1851
Under Cat. No.517 (illustrated)

287 TOILET GLASS
*c.*1865
Mahogany

The oval frame, faced with a simple hollow moulding, is suspended between U-shaped forks carved at the base and terminals with leafy scrolls; the upright support is screwed to a stepped oblong base with a veneered top and rounded ends, raised on bun feet. The brass ball and socket joints are impressed 'COPE & AUSTIN / PATENT'.
H.81(32); W.66(26); D28(11).

Similar mirrors bearing the label of Constantine of Leeds have been recorded.

PROV: Claremont Nursing Home, Clarendon Road, Leeds; given by the Trustees 1970. [14/70]

288 FOLDING TOILET GLASS
Probably early 20th century
Walnut

The lower stage is formed of two hinged boards which open like a trestle; the front panel is inset with a pivoted oval face mirror and the backboard supports a tall folding arm which projects forward with a circular mirror mounted on the end adjusted to reflect the hair or wig in the lower glass. The apparatus folds into a flat compact unit convenient for travelling or storing in a drawer.
H. extended 99 (39).

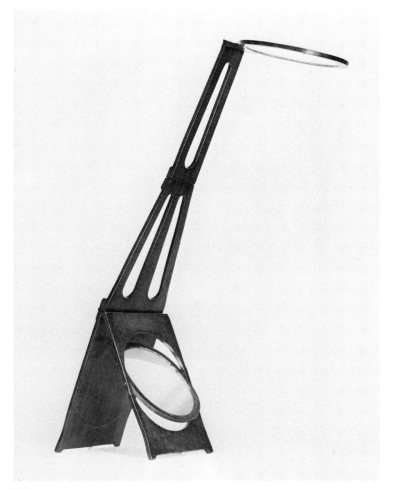

288

Several types of toilet glass contrived to provide an overhead reflection were made during the Victorian period. Heal's 1856–7 catalogue illustrates one with a turned frame and telescopic brass rod. Although this example is conceived in the 'Queen Anne' style, the openwork arm reveals a modern design attitude.

LIT: *L.A.C.*, No.32–3 (1956), p.26 & p.29 repr.

EXH: Sheffield Mappin Art Gallery, *Reflections*, 1972 (7).

PROV: Henry Priestley, Woodlands, Harrogate; sold on the premises by his executors 11 July 1955 (Hollis & Webb, Leeds) lot 1800; bought 1955.   [22.1/55]

MUSICAL INSTRUMENTS

289 BENTSIDE SPINET
*c.*1700
Walnut and oak; pine, sycamore, fruitwood, maple

The original stand with five baluster and bobbin-turned supports, united by pegged rails and stretchers, follows the gracefully curved and straight sided plan of the instrument; the front accommodates a long slant-back drawer originally fitted with a lidded till on the left-hand side. The drop-front case is of walnut combined with a pine base and back; the inner sides, walnut wrest plank and oak nameboard are faced with pine, the latter member being fronted by a panel of seaweed marquetry, featuring a central shell between paired fish and birds executed in ebonized fruitwood on a maple ground outlined by strings. The natural keys have ebony slips with papered fronts and the accidentals are of ivory, the two lowest being divided, giving a short bass octave and a compass of GG to d''; the pine key staves actuate lead-weighted sycamore jacks numbered in ink 1–54 with quill plectra and hog's bristle return springs; the interior retains its original jack-rail, bridge and pine sound board. The brass

289

strap hinges and locking plates of fanciful gothic design and the stamped brass lion's-mask ring handles are not original. H.87 (34½); W.162 (64); D.59 (23).

The instrument is unsigned, but a spinet of closely similar form and decorative treatment by Stephen Keene of London is illustrated in *Connoisseur*, May 1969 (advert. of Barling).

PROV: Mrs G. H. Pother; W. Waddingham (Antiques); bought 1962. [21/62]

290 HURDY-GURDY (French)
By T. Henry, Mirecourt
18th century, third quarter
Maple; sycamore, ebony

Guitar-shaped body, the belly, edged with an obliquely chequered band of ebony and ivory, is pierced by two C-sound holes and mounted with a stay pin to disengage one string; the peg box carved with a female head and incised diaper patterns continues on the line of the keybox; the resin-rimmed wheel turned by an ivory crank handle, bridge and ebonized tailpiece are of sycamore. The instrument has two melody strings with a compass of two octaves and four drone strings (gros bourdon, bourdon, trompette, monche). The keybox is indistinctly branded 'THOURENEL HENRY A MIRECOURT' the words forming a triangle around the ringed initials 'T.H.'. Wheel guard and tuning peg on the tailpiece missing; keybox lid renewed; the keyblades wrongly assembled – only one original rosewood blade survives, the top set were probably of ivory; they should all be on the treble side.
L.64 (25).

R. Clemencic, *Old Muscial Instruments*, 1968, p. 111, figs. 122–3 illustrates a closely similar hurdy-gurdy by Pierre Louvet, Paris, signed and dated 1778.

PROV: G. Hutchinson (Antiques); given to the L.A.C.F. by Stanley Burton 1963. [L.A.C.F./F13]

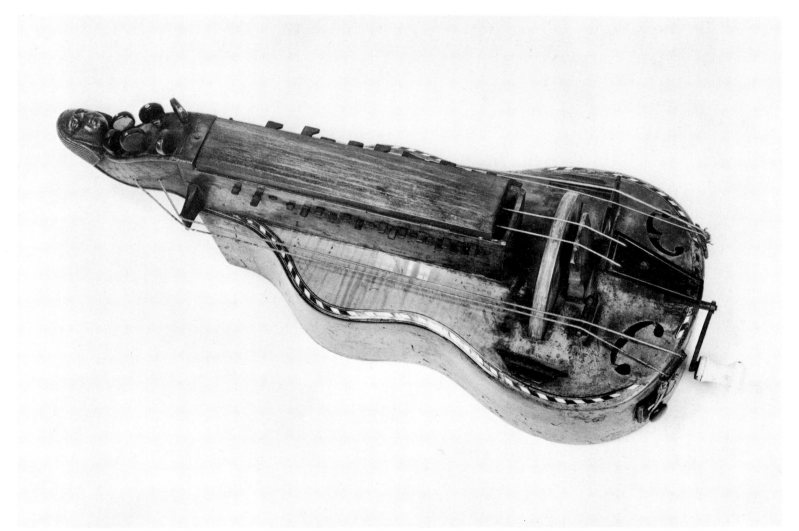

290

291, 292

291 HARP-LUTE

By Edward Light, London
*c.*1810
Pine

The lyre-shaped body, which stands on a low rectangular foot, is grained and varnished to simulate rosewood; the belly, pierced by a circular sound hole of sunburst design and decorated below the tied bridge with musical trophies, is styled with gilt borders of scrolled foliage, masks, cornucopia and vine trails; the arched back outlined with gilt borders contains a central slot. The neck, which rises from the treble-shoulder, has a wide ebonized fingerboard with eight ivory frets and three stepped nuts serving 1, 2–5, 6 & 7 strings; five longer strings are engaged to the swan-necked ridge, supported by a fluted pillar rising from the bass-shoulder; four of these strings can be raised a semi-tone by turning brass 'ring-stops', one blade being operated by a thumb crank; the twelve strings of gut and overspun silk are tuned by wrest pins. Pine body with gilt composition frond enrichment on the base and pillar. Inscribed in gold above the fingerboard '679 / Light / Foley Place / London'.
H.84 (33).

For fuller details see Cat. No.292.

PROV: Bought from Mallett & Son 1957. [14.2/57]

292 BRITISH HARP-LUTE

By Edward Light, London
*c.*1818
Pine; sycamore, beech

The body, set on a low oval foot, is grained and varnished to simulate rosewood; the back is made of seven splayed ribs edged with gilt oak-sprig trails and pierced by two sound slots and the belly, which originally centred on a carved rose, is painted with military trophies below the slanted pin bridge and outlined with gilt borders of scrolled foliage, cornucopia, masks and birds; the curved neck supports a small fingerboard with nine ivory frets for the two highest strings and rises to a pierced ridge set with wrest pins and ivory pegs. Of the nineteen strings thirteen are provided with lettered ditals which raise the pitch a semi-tone, the spring-lever action being fitted in a shielded recess behind the neck; the fluted pillar is painted with two dancers in classical dress; the capital and foot are banded with gilt composition ornament. Pine body, sycamore neck and pillar, beech shield. The instrument is painted in gold on the top of the body 'Light / Foley Place / London' with the word 'Patent' and the Royal Arms alongside. The dital cavity is impressed '195'.
H.86 (34).

For a discussion of Harp-Lutes and the work of Edward Light, the London organist who invented them, see Anthony Baines, *Catalogue of Musical Instruments in the Victoria & Albert Museum*, II, 1968, pp.62–8. Edward Light devised the Harp-Guitar about 1798, followed a few years later by his Harp-Lute with twelve and later fourteen strings. In 1816 Light patented his British Harp-Lute which included extra strings and a system of finger keys for raising the pitch; in 1819 he called his final model the Dital-Harp. All versions were played with both hands.

PROV: Bought from Mallett & Son, 1957. [14.1/57]

293 SQUARE PIANOFORTE

By John Longman, London
*c.*1812–15
Mahogany; satinwood, rosewood, maple, pine, oak, beech

The instrument is supported on six turned legs with decorative reeding, ebonized rings, brass collars and socket castors, the shafts screw into blocks mounted with stamped-brass roses; the instrument is of mahogany with a base and inner structures of pine and an oak back; there are three shallow drawers, the central one recessed, beneath the keyboard, with turned rosewood knobs and impressed location numbers '10, 11, 12'. The top and sides are outlined with chequered harlequin strings and brass beading; the folding drop-front opens to reveal a satinwood nameboard banded in rosewood with fretted end panels and a printed label inscribed 'J. LONGMAN / 131 CHEAPSIDE / LONDON / PATENT', the words imposed on an idealized scene of Apollo playing his lyre, various *amorini* and books of music. The hinged top has a turn-back flap on the right-hand side, and a lidded tuning-lever box on the left stamped behind '442'; the interior is fitted with a folding music rest and overlain by a green-painted pine dust cover; the lower pine sound board is inscribed in ink 'Wetherell', the wrest plank, veneered in maple, is lettered in the same hand and the beech bridge is impressed 'R P'. The ivory and ebony keys on sycamore staves with lead inserts number sixty-eight and give a compass of FF to C''', the top ten notes being 'additional keys', an innovation which extended the compass without enlarging the case, the extra notes being in a separate frame, the hammers rising through a slot in the soundboard. English double-action with over dampers and leather hammer cover-

293

293

ing; bi-chord throughout, the lower notes overspun; single sustaining pedal lifting the dampers.
H.87 (34½); L.168 (66); D.61 (24).

Longman & Co were dealers in musical instruments and published muscial scores but did not manufacture keyboard instruments themselves. They traded at 131, Cheapside between 1802 and 1816 when a partnership with Herron was formed. Six turned supports rather than a frame-stand on four legs, suggests a date after 1810.

PROV: Bequeathed by Mrs D. U. McGrigor Phillips of Temple Sowerby Manor, Penrith 1967.   [24.37/67]

294 PEDAL-HARP
By Sebastian Erard, London
1815
Pine, birch, sycamore, beech, mahogany

The frame is japanned black with gilt-composition enrich-

ments in the Grecian taste; the fluted pillar has classical foliage at its base and the capital, finished in two-colour gold, bears three winged caryatid figures in moulded relief holding chaplets inscribed: 'S. ERARD / PUBLISH'D / APRIL 19 / 1811'; the veneered pine belly is styled with delicate borders surrounding two transfer-printed figures playing instruments and the sound box is backed by five hinged traps engraved with musicians, and actuated by a pedal; the string holes are outlined with ivory darts. The curved mahogany neck is set with forty-three wrench pins and brass side plates supporting a double row of pedal operated *fourchettes* by which each string can be raised either a semi-tone or a full tone. One plate is engraved 'Sebastian Erard's / Patent No 1954 / 18, Great Marlborough Street, LONDON' adjoining the royal coat of arms. The base, ornamented with angels and anthemion motifs in gilt-composition, is raised on four paw feet and has seven brass pedals fitted in double-notched slots; the inner structures are of sycamore, beech and pine; the bottom is impressed '1985'.
H.170 (67); W.81 (32).

The relevant entry in Erard's stock book reads:
'1954 Miss Pigou
D   Hill St. Berk Sq.
         28th February 1815'

PROV: Georgiana Pigou married Hugo Charles Meynell in 1819; he took the additional surname of Ingram on succeeding to the Temple Newsam estates in 1841; by descent to the Earls of Halifax; given by Lord Halifax 1922.

[1922/F10]

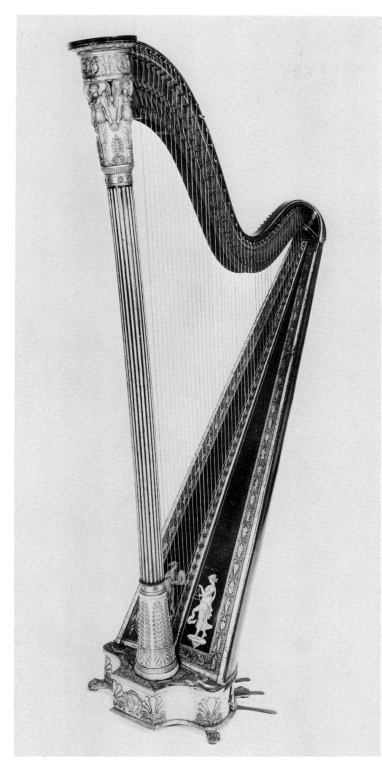

294

295

295 CABINET UPRIGHT PIANOFORTE

By John Broadwood & Sons, London
c.1830
Rosewood; mahogany, oak, pine, elm, beech, sycamore

The veneered rosewood case with a mahogany foundation is fronted by a panel of textile stained purple and painted with floral designs in the Chinese taste; the cornice, enriched with leaf mouldings in gilt composition, is supported by corner colonettes with lotus capitals and inlaid mother of pearl bases, the shafts being japanned with oriental scenes; a carved and gilt figure of a seated cupid holding a lyre and scroll once perched on the top; the sides are bordered with floral trails in gold paint. The hinged cover, fitted with a folding music rest, opens to reveal ivory and ebony keys, quarter-round candle slides and the nameboard with a foliate pattern in brass centering on a tablet inscribed 'John Broadwood & Sons / Makers to his Majesty & the Princesses / Great Pultney Street, Golden Square London'. The keyboard is supported at the front by two carved and gilt legs of Louis XIV fronded vase design; the lower stage is enclosed by panelled doors with gadrooned knobs, the rear castors have friction rollers. The sycamore key staves weighted with lead operate trackers connected to hammers at the top of the frame; there are seventy-three notes giving a compass FF to f''', sticker bi-chord action with two pedals. The main internal members are of oak and pine with a beech bridge, veneered wrest-pin rail and a brass hitch plate (patented by Broadwoods in 1827).

H.188 (74); W.114 (65); D.64 (25).

Many components are inscribed in pencil 'Cossow 4979'; the lowest key is signed in ink 'Henderson 4979' and the upright tracker frame is impressed 'J.W. Benton'. Other inscriptions include 'F.1. 4979'; 'E.B'; 'Tuned by Jas Smith'; 'Messrs Smith & (?) Leeds' and various faint graffiti.

The case of this instrument has been lavishly styled to harmonize with the glamorous Chinese Drawing Room at Temple Newsam created by Lady Hertford about 1830. The main features of her interior were a hand-painted Chinese wallpaper depicting a garden scene, wall-cabinets incorporating panels of Japanese lacquer bordered by leafy floral trails, richly carved door cases and surrounds taken from a Louis XIV period French château and various florid gilt ornaments. The piano case reflects all these decorative elements; structural evidence suggests later styling to harmonize with the decor; the original design probably resembled a model made by Broadwood & Sons in 1834 now at the University of Edinburgh, *Russell Collection Catalogue*, 1968, No.26, repr. The instrument was almost certainly acquired and embellished by Lady Hertford (d.1834) a woman renowned for her frivolous taste, who cut out the plates from her subscription copy of J. J. Audubon's *Birds of America* to enhance the walls of her Chinese drawing room.

LIT: C. G. Gilbert, 'Lady Hertford, John James Audubon and the Chinese Drawing Room at Temple Newsam', *L.A.C.*, No.61 (1968), pp.14–17.

EXH: Temple Newsam, *Pictures and Furniture*, 1938 (44).

PROV: By descent from Lady Hertford to the Earl of Halifax; given 1922. [1922/F11]

296 PEDAL-HARP AND CASE
By Sebastian and Pierre Erard, London
1845
Bird's-eye maple; rosewood, pine, sycamore, beech

The frame is veneered in bird's-eye maple and styled in the gothic taste with gilt-composition enrichments; the pillar,

ribbed with gilt tracery, is lavishly decorated with gothic foliage, the capital being headed by six applied moulded reliefs of angels standing in canopied niches with scrolls inscribed 'Pierre Erard / Published Dec'r 10 1835', the legend is repeated on the faceted base. The soundbox, bordered with rosewood and gilt lines has five traps in the back actuated by a pedal; the curved neck is faced with brass plates and bears wrench pins engaging nine overspun and thirty-six gut strings, which can be raised a semi or a full tone by operating seven pedals which activate a double row of *fourchettes*. One side is engraved 'Sebastian Erard's / Patent No.5743 / 18, Great Marlborough Street, LONDON' with the royal coat of arms, the other is inscribed, 'Sebastian Erard / Harp & Piano forte maker in Ordinary TO HER Majesty AND THE ROYAL FAMILY'. The gilt base is raised on 'gargoyle' feet, the underside being impressed (twice) '5716'. The frame is composed of a beech neck and sycamore pillar, a pine belly and birch back; the inner structures are of sycamore and beech.

H.170 (67); W.89 (35).

The original plank pine case braced with iron corner straps has a hinged door secured by hook and eye latches and a lock; the interior is lined with green baize and leather pads; each side is branded 'ERARD' and with the number '157'.

The entry against 5743 in Erard's stock book reads:
'Miss Gascoigne   May 1st 1846
No.3 Parlington Square, Leeds
Maple, Gothic
December 1845'.

PROV: The harp was evidently bought by one of R.O. Gascoigne's daughters Mary Isabella and Elizabeth who succeeded him in 1843 and, whilst unmarried, lived together at Parlington Hall, Yorkshire. An inventory of the house taken that year (G.C./F 4/5) records 'Large Drawing Room – Harp by Erard' – showing that they already owned one instrument. By descent to Sir Alvary Gascoigne; the Gascoigne gift 1968. [7.194/68]

296

296

297 CONCERT GRAND PIANOFORTE
Action by Erard; the case by Marsh and Jones, Leeds
*c.*1870
Satinwood; rosewood, walnut, mahogany, sycamore, etc., pine, oak

The satinwood case is outlined with walnut and ebony bands alternating with star medallions, the lower edge bordered by a lobe-and-dog-tooth pattern; the treble-side frames three parcel-gilt panels incorporating gothic roses executed in marquetry on an ebonized ground and the keyboard cover is enriched with gothic ornament in stained and shaded woods. A section of the top folds back to reveal a music rest flanked by candle slides of trefoil design. The case rests on three massive block turned columns linked by a long side and shorter front stretcher rail supporting the pedal box, the whole underframe is richly styled with chamfers, decorative inlay and carved lotus capitals headed by floral corbels. The base board and inner structures are of oak and pine incorporating a metal hitch-plate and four iron braces; brass castors stamped 'COPE & COLLINSON'.
H.94 (37); L.244 (96); W.137 (54).

Erard special repetition double escapement action with under dampers and felt hammers serving eighty-five ivory and ebony keys giving a seven octave compass AAA to a''''; tri-chord except for the lowest 17 notes which are overspun bi-chord (8) and single (9); damper and *una corda* pedals.

297 (Colour frontispiece Vol. I)

The cover, which functions when raised as a nameboard, is inlaid 'CASE DESIGNED & EXECUTED BY / MARSH & JONES MAN'RS LEEDS / PATENT ERARD LONDON'; the interior is impressed (twice) '10724' and 'C. MARTIN'; the lowest key stave is stamped 'J. BROOKS' and 'COURTICE', while the top note is impressed 'Chevalier'. An under brace bears the maker's printed paper label 'Marsh & Jones / (Late Kendell & Co.,) / LEEDS / No. *18112* / Workman's Name *Marshall*'. The impressed number 10724 may indicate the action dates from *c.*1838–40, especially as the piano is narrow towards the tail, and that the instrument was re-cased by Marsh & Jones as part of a more extensive furnishing programme.

John Marsh & Edward Jones were in partnership from 1864–1872 when Henry Cribb joined the firm. They made a strikingly similar grand piano to the design of Charles Bevan for Titus Salt, jnr. in 1867, illustrated in *The Building News*, 1 March 1867, with an X-framed 'Ottoman duet stool' and a music canterbury *en suite*. (An almost identical duet stool made to accompany the Leeds piano was extant until about 1960.) The V. & A. possess an unsigned drawing attributed to Bevan for a third grand piano styled in the same reformed gothic taste (E.16/1915, nos.603 & 606 in vol.95B.28). The fact that the Salt piano is inlaid on the nameboard 'C. Bevan del', whereas this example is inscribed 'Case Designed & Executed by Marsh & Jones' implies that, although powerfully influenced by Bevan's concepts the Leeds firm did not commission him to supply the design (see cat. No.521a).

LIT: *L.A.C.*, No.25 (1954) p.6, repr.; L. O. J. Boynton, 'High Victorian Furniture: The Example of Marsh & Jones of Leeds', *Furniture History*, III (1967) p.60, pls.20 & 21;

S.Jervis, *Victorian Furniture*, 1968, pl.61; M. I. Wilson, 'The Case of the Victorian Piano' *V. & A. Year Book III* (1972), pp.135–7, fig.3.

PROV: The Earl of Darnley; Heckmondwike Grammar School; given by the headmaster C. J. S. Kyte 1954.

[4/54]

ORGAN, walnut
By Wordsworth & Maskell, Leeds
to the design of G. F. Bodley, 1877
Under Cat. No.534 (illustrated)

298 BOUDOIR GRAND PIANOFORTE (French)
Action by Erard; the case by Jansen, Paris
1900
Rosewood, satinwood, mahogany, walnut, sycamore, fruitwood, oak, pine, various coloured woods

The case, lavishly veneered with pictorial marquetry incorporating emblems, is supported on four cabriole legs and richly ornamented with chased and gilt bronze mounts. The decoration is closely based on J. H. Riesener's celebrated 'Bureau du Roi Louis XV' (hereafter B d R) at Versailles. The flat top, surrounded by a brass moulding and an interlaced border, is formed of a hinged fold-back front section inset with three marquetry compositions of musical and classical trophies between floral bouquets (copied from the shelf top of B d R); the larger, tapering panel centres on an elaborate trophy representing Learning and the Arts flanked by circular medallions enclosing on the left attributes of Dramatic Poetry and on the right those of Lyric Poetry (all three designs are taken from the roll-cover of B d R); two subsidiary panels depict a fronded whorl and a floral spray. The roundels incorporate inscribed ribbons and documents (see below for transcription). The straight and bent sides of the case are each styled with an identical pair of pictorial panels representing naval and military trophies (copied from the upper ends of B d R) centering on an oval floral medallion; the treble end is decorated with a marine composition

298

of shells, coral, pearls, seaweed, etc., the bass end is inset with fruit and the tail panel with flowers (all based on marquetry details from B d R); the keyboard cover is faced with marquetry panels enclosing trophies emblematic of, to the right Astronomy and to the left Mathematics (derived from the back of B d R with elements from Wallace collection No. F.102), the terrestrial globe is inscribed 'NORD, MEDITERANEE, MER ARAGULES PESEN'. The sides are mounted with heavy swags, beribboned wreaths and massive paired cornucopia; the keeled, tapering cabriole legs on castors are set with lion pelts connected by reeding to fronded *sabots* and the lower edge is continuously bordered with gilt-bronze foliage (nearly all the mounts are reproduced from B d R with the exception of a corner ornament formed as a tree with tabor and bagpipes). The keyboard cover functions, when lifted, as the nameboard, inlaid in ivory 'Erard' and a

section of the top hinges back to reveal a folding mahogany music rest flanked by candleslides designed as shaped panels of floral marquetry with brass borders. The lyre-shaped pedal box is set with acanthus mounts and a female sunburst mask. Pine underframe and sound board, oak sides and legs, the interior veneered in bird's-eye maple and fitted with a brass hitchplate and bracing frame. The top of the piano displays two medallions, the one representing Dramatic Poetry includes two ribbons inscribed 'NON. NISI. GRANDIA. CANTO' and 'IRRIDENS. CUSPIDE. FIGO.' also an open book engraved 'O muses qui regnez / dans le céleste / empire / Dites ce qui aux / mortels vous seul / pouvez dire / chastes divinitès / à qui dans / l'univers / / Tous les temps Tous les lieux / sont à la fois / ouverts / La seule / renommé / nous insp / A guide.' The other roundel, emblematic of Lyric Poetry incorporates two ribbons inscribed 'BREVI.

COMPLECTOR. SINGULAVANI.' and 'PASTORUM. CARMINA. LUDC.'.
H.101 (40); L.229 (90); W.152 (60).

Erards repetition grand action having a seven octave compass AAA to a'''' with under-dampers and felt hammers; tri-chord except for the lowest strings which are overspun bi-chord (6) and single (11); damper and *una corda* pedals. The highest and lowest key-staves and the music rest are impressed '80061', the interior is stamped 'FINEL' and 'DAVID' and stencilled '80061'. Michel's *Piano Atlas*, 1957, p.65 records that Erards commenced the year 1900 with the serial number 80,000.

According to information communicated by Monsieur S. A. Pleyel, Erards ledgers contain the following entry:
'Piano No.80061
Piano à queue – model 1 – en blanc Marqueterie et bronzes par JANSEN, Ebèniste.
Mai 1901 – vendu à LONDRES.
The firm of M. Jansen still survives as high class cabinet makers and house furnishers.

LIT: *The British Home Today*, ed. W. Shaw Sparrow, 1904, p. xviii (advertising supplement) illustrates this model described as 'Style of Louis XV, is in Marquetrie designs to match the famous Bureau de Régent by Reisener with Extra Rich Ormolu Mounts, chased to rival the work of Gouthière.'

EXH: Paris, International Exhibition, 1900.
The souvenir catalogue of the Sam Wilson collection, opened 12 Oct. 1925 (Leeds Art Gallery) states that the instrument (No.219) was made expressly for the above exhibition. No complete catalogues were published but a reference to this piano occurs in *Rapports du Jury International*, Group III, classes 11–18, Paris, 1902, p.521; the passage notes 'C'est une vraie merveille d'ébénisterie, valant 50,000 francs.'

PROV: Acquired by Sam Wilson for Rutland Lodge, Leeds; the Sam Wilson Bequest 1925.   [S.W.219]

PICTURE FRAMES

299 PICTURE FRAME
*c.*1685
Lime

The elaborately carved and pierced cresting centres on crossed palm boughs supporting floral garlands and a bouquet of flowers, fir-cones and fruit; the upper corners are surmounted by tied laurel wreaths with a cowrie shell on the right and a cluster of three winged cherub heads beneath; the lower sides are carved with heavy drapes festooned with fruit, blossom and wheat ears; the bottom rail is decorated with crossed laurel and oak sprays intertwined with fir-cones, pea-pods and swags of orchard fruit, roses and lilies; the moulded inner surround is enriched with berried leaf trails.
H.183 (72); W.157 (62).

A heavy coat of brown paint was removed in 1947 and about the same time a Victorian mirror plate was replaced by the oil portrait of the 1st Earl of Craven.

The name of Grinling Gibbons has inevitably been associated with this spectacular frame, but documentary evidence is lacking. Although the overall design and decorative vocabulary display analogies with Gibbons' proven compositions the craftsmanship is not fine enough to justify a attribution to his workshop and suggests the hand of a follower such as Jonathan Maine.

LIT: *Apollo*, July 1946, p. xxii, repr.; *L.A.C.*, No.2 (1947), p.3, repr.; R. Fastnedge, *English Furniture Styles, 1500–1830*, 1955, pl.18; D. Green, *Grinling Gibbons*, 1964, p.146.

PROV: By descent from the Tortman family of Syston Court, Gloucestershire to Major F. B. N. Dickenson; J. E. Rawlins; Syston Court sale (Norfolk & Prior) 21–23 May 1935, lot 84, repr.; Wilfred Gosling (Antiques); Hotspur, Ltd; bought with the aid of a government grant 1947.   [10/47]

300 PICTURE FRAME
*c.*1730
Pine

Of architectural design with side pendants, corner rosettes and an inset bottom rail with oak swags centering on an acanthus spray; the outer moulding carved with egg and dart, the inner border of twisted-ribbon and floret pattern with an angular fret between; originally painted green, now gilt.
H.114 (45); W.110 (43½).

Apart from the oak swags and acanthus clasp the frame corresponds precisely to the overmantel surround of a chimneypiece designed by William Kent for Sir William Strickland published in Isaac Ware's *Designs of Inigo Jones and Others,*

300

1735, pl.31. This frame was obviously once part of a chimneypiece (splayed grooves on the back show where the pediment was secured), but since neither of the two Kentian style chimneypieces at Boynton match the lower stage of this engraving the overmantel may have come from the Strickland's London house. It is perhaps relevant that Kent was born at Bridlington, only a few miles from Boynton and about 1730 Lord Burlington was consulted about alterations.

The painting by P. Casteels has been artificially extended along the top and sides to fit the frame, the back of which is inscribed in pencil 'This side Green / ? Oak Room Door / Front Hall Door'.

LIT: *L.A.C.*, No.14 (1950–1), p.8 and p.11, repr.

PROV: By descent from Sir William Strickland, 4th Baronet of Boynton Hall, Yorkshire, to the Rev. J. E. Strickland; bought at the Boynton Hall sale (Henry Spencer,Retford) 21–23 Nov. 1950, lot 386.   [42.6/50]

301–306 PICTURE FRAMES
There are too many fine picture frames in the Leeds collection for individual mention, accordingly reference can be made only to certain outstandingly decorative or historically interesting examples.

The earliest of note is a mid seventeenth century carved and gilt frame containing a full-length *Portrait of Sir Arthur Ingram*, d.1642, elaborately styled in the auricular manner

300

with flattish scrolls, fleshy leaves and gristle, winged bird heads on the shoulders and grotesque masks on the rails. The frame surrounding Gerard Soest's *Portrait of a General* is boldly enriched with a pulvinated bay leaf moulding and a running pattern of husks bordered by waterleaf – a treatment datable to *c*.1675. The school of Grinling Gibbons is represented by an important limewood frame, the subject of a full

entry (Cat. No.299) and an example copied from one of William Kent's designs is also catalogued separately (Cat. No.300).

Among the Temple Newsam family portraits given by the Earl of Halifax in 1948 are three contained within magnificent rococo frames; no documentation has been traced, but they clearly date from the 7th Viscount Irwin's time.

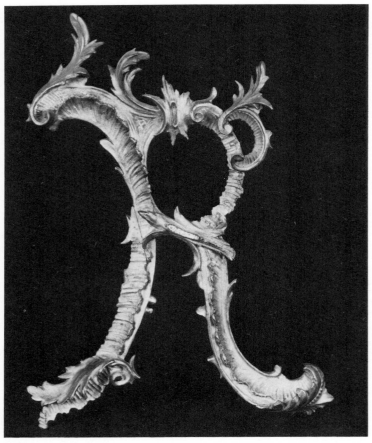

303

305

A gilt pair, presumably designed to grace his imposing new saloon furnished in 1746, are vigorously styled with pierced flamework surrounds, long foliate scrolls and crested by baskets of fruit and flowers (Cat. No.301). The third rococo frame, enclosing a full-length *Portrait of Miss Ingram* is flamboyantly carved with a system of long leafy scrolls, floral festoons and an open pediment featuring a basket of fruit, the stripped pine was formerly painted (Cat. No.302). The Agnes and Norman Lupton bequest included a highly decorative frame for a miniature in carved and gilt pine, the small oval opening being formed by the loop of a letter R embellished with fanciful rococo borders and fronded scrolls (Cat. No. 303). The design is reminiscent of Hubert Gravelot's engraved initial letters.

In England, during the last quarter of the century so-called 'Carlo Maratti' picture frames – a standard pattern of concave profile embellished with classical mouldings – were widely favoured; two handsome versions with running acanthus and twisted-ribbon borders accommodate Sir Joshua Reynolds' full length *Portrait of Lady Hertford* (1781) and Batoni's *Portrait of Sir Thomas Gascoigne* (1778). The collection also contains an impressive silvered and gilt late seventeenth century Italian prototype of this design framing *St. James the Greater* by Carlo Maratta who gave his name to the pattern.

Two Victorian gilt frames deserve mention – each almost certainly designed by the artist. The earlier, made for Holman Hunt's *The Shadow of Death* (1873), is patterned with geometric chip-carved interlace panels expressive of Moorish decorative traditions suiting the biblical subject; it displays interesting affinities with progressive furniture styles of the period and includes an exotic inner border faced with ivory strips (Cat. No.304). The other painting, Lord Leighton's *The Return of Persephone* (1891), is set in a grandiose architectural frame with fluted Ionic pilasters supporting a rich anthemion frieze outlined by classical mouldings (Cat. No. 305).

An ebonized frame with gilt mouldings surrounding an early nineteenth century watercolour in the Gascoigne collection (Cat. No.306) bears the trade label of 'Staveleys, / CARVERS & GILDERS, / removed into Stonegate, / YORK / . . . .' Their label has also been noted on several picture frames at Burton Constable, near Hull.

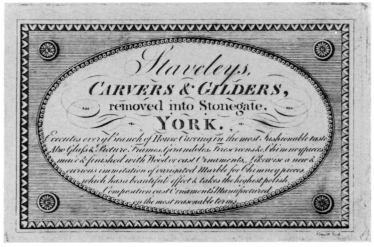

306